Thank you...

...for purchasing this copy of Numeracy Today for ages 5-7. We hope that you will find these 60 photocopiable pages helpful as part of your programme for the Numeracy Hour.

The sheets can be photocopied onto paper, card or overhead projector transparencies. Each sheet is preceded by an introductory page giving ideas, suggestions and answers where appropriate.

Please note that photocopies can only be made for use by the purchasing institution. Supplying copies to other schools, institutions or individuals breaches the copyright licence. Thank you for your help in this.

This Numeracy Today book is part of our growing range of educational titles. Most of our books are individual workbooks but, due to popular demand, we are now introducing a greater number of photocopiable titles especially for teachers. You may like to look out for:

Numeracy Today for ages 7-9
ISBN 1897737 63 7

Numeracy Today for ages 9-11
ISBN 1897737 58 0

To find details of our other publications,
please visit our website:

www.acblack.com

Doubles

$1 + 1 = 2$

$2 + 2 = 4$

$3 + 3 = 6$

$4 + 4 = 8$

$5 + 5 = 10$

$6 + 6 = 12$

$7 + 7 = 14$

$8 + 8 = 16$

$9 + 9 = 18$

$10 + 10 = 20$

$11 + 11 = 22$

$12 + 12 = 24$

$13 + 13 = 26$

$14 + 14 = 28$

$15 + 15 = 30$

$20 + 20 = 40$

$25 + 25 = 50$

$30 + 30 = 60$

$35 + 35 = 70$

$40 + 40 = 80$

$45 + 45 = 90$

$50 + 50 = 100$

NUMERACY TODAY
© Andrew Brodie Publications ✓ www.acblack.com

NUMERACY TODAY *for ages 5 - 7* CONTENTS PAGE

1 Number Cards (1)

2 Number Cards (2)

3 Vocabulary Cards (1)

4 Vocabulary Cards (2)

5 Place Value Cards

6 The Hundred Square

7 Blank Hundred Square

8 Number Flashcards (1)

9 Number Flashcards (2)

10 Bits of the Square

11 Numbers in Words (1)

12 Numbers in Words (2)

13 4 x 4 Number Squares

14 5 x 5 Number Squares

15 6 x 6 Number Squares

16 Random Spot Dominoes (1)

17 Random Spot Dominoes (2)

18 Domino Spot Count

19 Data Handling: Block Graph

20 Data Handling: Pictogram

21 Bond Cards - Addition to 6

22 Bond Cards - Addition from 7 to 9

23 Bonds of 10

24 Bond Cards - Subtraction 9, 8 & 7

25 Bond Cards - Subtraction 6,5,4,3,2 & 1

26 Bonds of 20 (1)

27 Bonds of 20 (2)

28 Bonds: Target Setting

29 Bonds of 100

30 Counting (1)

31 Counting (2)

32 Counting (3)

33 Numbers in Sequence

34 Numbers Game

35 Number Track (1)

36 Number Track (2)

37 Number Track (3)

38 Number Track (4)

39 Leapfrogs and Numbers (1)

40 Leapfrogs and Numbers (2)

41 Shapes (1)

42 Shapes (2)

43 Shapes (3)

44 Vocabulary Cards (3)

45 Length to the Nearest Centimetre (1)

46 Length to the Nearest Centimetre (2)

47 Symmetrical Reflections

48 Lines of Symmetry

49 Vocabulary Cards (4)

50 Vocabulary Cards (5)

51 Clock Face and Hands

52 Blank Clock Face

53 Clock Faces

54 Time: O'clocks

55 Time: Half Hours

56 Time: Quarter Past

57 Time: Quarter To

58 Analogue and Digital Clocks

59 Days of the Week

60 Months and Seasons

Number Cards (1)

The National Numeracy Strategy suggests that every child should have a set of digit cards, 0 to 9. The digit cards on Sheet 1 are designed to be copied onto card, or onto paper and laminated, then cut out. We suggest that each child is given a complete set of the cards. As they become more advanced in their numeracy work you may wish to provide children with some of the cards on Sheet 2.

The cards can be used:

… for children to hold up when a specific number is stated by the teacher

… for children to hold up to show the answer to an addition or subtraction question

… for children to sort into the correct order

… by the teacher showing pupils pairs of the cards to identify and to state which is the smaller number and which is the larger number

… for children to put into order then to use for counting on - for example, the children can be asked to start at three and to count on to seven. (They should be encouraged to point at the 3 card first but then to make 'jumps' with their fingers, saying the name of each number as they arrive at it: *'four, five,six, seven.'* They could be asked how many jumps they have made.)

… for children to put into order then to use for counting back - for example, the children can be asked to start at nine and to count back to two. (They should be encouraged to point at the 9 card first but then to make 'jumps' with their fingers, saying the name of each number as they arrive at it: *'eight, seven, six, five, four, three, two.'* They could be asked how many jumps they have made.)

You may wish to copy the whole sheet onto an OHP transparency to talk about the numbers with the children, counting on or back together for example.

You may like to copy the whole sheet onto card or paper to put onto the wall for use during discussions.

Number Cards (1)

1	2	3
4	5	6
7	8	q

Number Cards (2)

As with Sheet 1, the digit cards are designed to be copied onto card then cut out. They could be laminated before being cut out if possible. We suggest that each child is given some of the cards, together with a complete set of those on Sheet 1, as they become more advanced in their numeracy skills. A Reception child might have only the cards on Sheet 1, plus the zero card from this sheet. A Year 2 child might need to have all the cards.

The cards can be used in the same way as those on Sheet 1 but the extra cards also permit other uses. Pupils in Year 1 or Year 2 can be encouraged to use the cards to create number sentences such as:

You could ask the children how many addition sentences they can make using only the cards provided. So, in each equation, they can only use a number once as they only have one copy of each number. You could start, during an oral work session, with only allowing digit cards from 1 to 5:

$$1 + 2 = 3 \qquad 2 + 1 = 3 \qquad 3 + 1 = 4 \qquad 4 + 1 = 5$$
$$1 + 3 = 4 \qquad 2 + 3 = 5 \qquad 3 + 2 = 5$$
$$1 + 4 = 5$$

Now the pupils could work in pairs to try the same again, this time using digit cards from 1 to 6:

$$1 + 2 = 3 \qquad 2 + 1 = 3 \qquad 3 + 1 = 4 \qquad 4 + 1 = 5 \qquad 5 + 1 = 6$$
$$1 + 3 = 4 \qquad 2 + 3 = 5 \qquad 3 + 2 = 5 \qquad 4 + 2 = 6$$
$$1 + 4 = 5 \qquad 2 + 4 = 6$$
$$1 + 5 = 6$$

Some pupils will find this type of work very stimulating. They can extend the activity further by going up to seven, eight or nine. The digit card zero can also be introduced.

Pupils can move on to creating subtraction sentences.

Advanced pupils will be able to create sentences using the 'greater than' and 'less than' cards, such as:

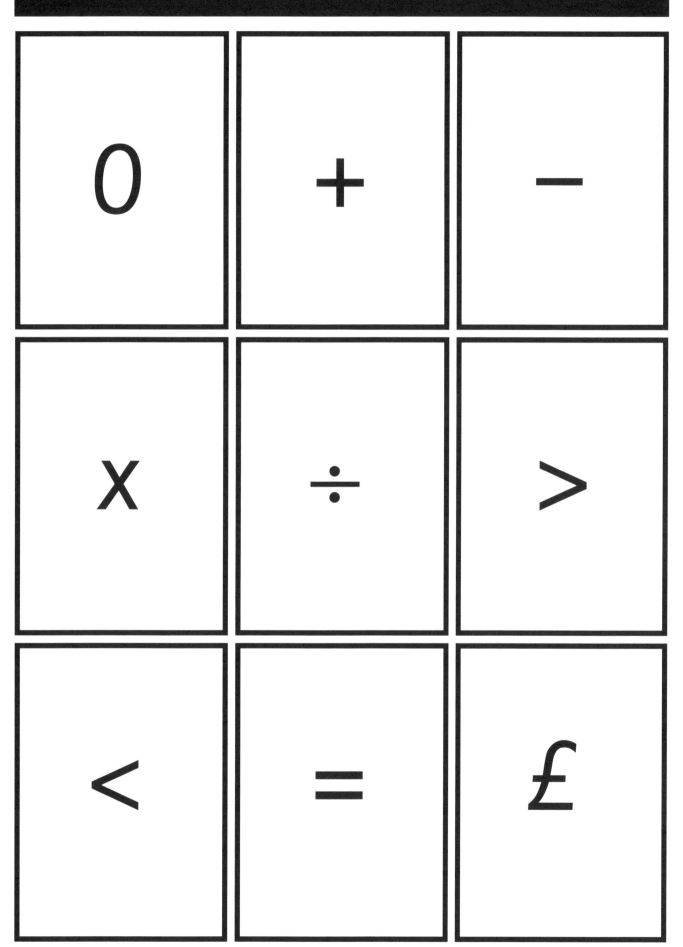

Vocabulary Cards (1)

The vocabulary cards are designed to be copied onto card then cut out. They could be laminated before being cut out if this is possible.

The children will learn many mathematical words orally during their numeracy lessons. The National Numeracy Strategy provides a comprehensive list within the *Mathematical Vocabulary* supplement. We have selected some of the ones which the children will use most often. You may like to introduce the cards gradually, introducing a new card every day and reminding pupils of those which they have seen before. The 'zero' card can be introduced at the same time as the concept of zero. Examining the words carefully together can help to promote pupils' literacy skills at the same time as extending their vocabulary for numeracy.

The cards can be used:

... as flashcards for reading number names

... as spelling cards for pupils to copy

... on a wall display of numeracy vocabulary

... for matching to the digit cards on Sheet 1.

zero 0	one 1
two 2	three 3
four 4	five 5
six 6	seven 7
eight 8	nine 9
ten 10	eleven 11
twelve 12	thirteen 13
fourteen 14	fifteen 15
sixteen 16	seventeen 17

Vocabulary Cards (2)

The vocabulary cards are designed to be copied onto card then cut out. They could be laminated before being cut out if this is possible.

The children will learn many mathematical words orally during their numeracy lessons. The National Numeracy Strategy provides a comprehensive list within the *Mathematical Vocabulary* supplement. We have selected some of the ones which the children will use most often. You may like to introduce the cards gradually, introducing a new card every day and reminding pupils of those which they have seen before. The 'zero' card can be introduced at the same time as the concept of zero. Examining the words carefully together can help to promote pupils' literacy skills at the same time as extending their vocabulary for numeracy.

As with those on Sheet 3, the cards can be used:

... as flashcards for reading number names and other mathematical vocabulary

... as spelling cards for pupils to copy

... on a wall display of numeracy vocabulary.

eighteen 18	nineteen 19
twenty 20	thirty 30
forty 40	fifty 50
sixty 60	seventy 70
eighty 80	ninety 90
hundred 100	add +
make	equals =
subtract —	plus +
minus 100	1+1=2 double

Place Value Cards

Sheet 5 should be copied onto card. The number cards should then be cut out to give this set:

0

100	10	1
200	20	2
300	30	3
400	40	4
500	50	5
600	60	6
700	70	7
800	80	8
900	90	9

Children need to be able to see and understand the value of every digit in a number.

The number cards on Sheet 5 can be used to create every number between 0 and 999. With Year 1 pupils you may decide only to use the units cards and the tens cards. The hundreds cards can then be introduced in Year 2.

Cards are placed over each other to create a number. For example, to create the number 642 we put the 40 card on top of the 600 card and the 2 card on the 40 card:

   ⟶

Place Value Cards

1 0 0	1 0	0
2 0 0	2 0	1
3 0 0	3 0	2
4 0 0	4 0	3
5 0 0	5 0	4
6 0 0	6 0	5
7 0 0	7 0	6
8 0 0	8 0	7
9 0 0	9 0	8
		9

The Hundred Square

The hundred square can be used:

... for counting on or back in tens. Children can start at a whole ten, eg 40, and count on in tens or start at another number, eg 17, and count on in tens. Similarly they can start at a higher number, eg 84, and count back in tens.

... for colouring in multiplication tables, (for example children can colour the three times table and see the pattern made - each multiplication table will make a different pattern so the pupils could have several copies of this sheet to enable them to show each of the tables)

... for shading all the multiples of 2 to show odd and even numbers

... as an aid to adding on or subtracting

The Hundred Square

1	2	3	4	5	6	7	8	9	10
11	12	13	14	15	16	17	18	19	20
21	22	23	24	25	26	27	28	29	30
31	32	33	34	35	36	37	38	39	40
41	42	43	44	45	46	47	48	49	50
51	52	53	54	55	56	57	58	59	60
61	62	63	64	65	66	67	68	69	70
71	72	73	74	75	76	77	78	79	80
81	82	83	84	85	86	87	88	89	90
91	92	93	94	95	96	97	98	99	100

Blank Hundred Square

The blank hundred square can be used:

... for children to make their own hundred square

... for the children to play a number game where they take it in turns to pick a number flashcard from a pile and write on the number in the correct place (number flashcards are provided on Sheet 8 and Sheet 9)

... by the teacher to mark on some of the numbers for pupils to complete the hundred square

... by the teacher to create a 0 to 99 square

... by the teacher to write the 0 and the 99 on a 0 to 99 square, then to ask the children to write on numbers selected by the teacher at random from the flashcards

1	2	3	4	5	6	7	8	9	10
11	12	13	14	15	16	17	18	19	20
21	22	23	24	25	26	27	28	29	30
31	32	33	34	35	36	37	38	39	40
41	42	43	44	45	46	47	48	49	50
51	52	53	54	55	56	57	58	59	60
61	62	63	64	65	66	67	68	69	70
71	72	73	74	75	76	77	78	79	80
81	82	83	84	85	86	87	88	89	90
91	92	93	94	95	96	97	98	99	100

Number Flashcards (1)

Year 2 pupils need to be able to read and write numbers to at least 100. Sheet 8 clearly presents the numbers 0 to 54. The numbers 55 to 109 are provided on Sheet 9.

This sheet is designed to be photocopied onto card so that individual flashcards can be made. You may wish to enlarge the sheet on the copier.

You could simply ask pupils to tell you what number is shown on each flashcard which you hold or you could present them with a set of the cards and ask them to find a particular number.

The cards can be used in conjunction with the blank hundred square on Sheet 7. Children can take turns picking a card from this set and writing the number it shows in the correct place on the hundred square. Alternatively, the teacher can pick out individual cards and ask the children to write the numbers on the blank hundred square or on the 0 to 99 square if preferred.

0	1	2	3	4
5	6	7	8	9
10	11	12	13	14
15	16	17	18	19
20	21	22	23	24
25	26	27	28	29
30	31	32	33	34
35	36	37	38	39
40	41	42	43	44
45	46	47	48	49
50	51	52	53	54

Number Flashcards (2)

Year 2 pupils need to be able to read and write numbers to at least 100. Sheet 9 clearly presents the numbers 55 to 109. The numbers 0 to 54 are provided on Sheet 8.

This sheet is designed to be photocopied onto card so that individual flashcards can be made. You may wish to enlarge the sheet on the copier.

You could simply ask pupils to tell you what number is shown on each flashcard which you hold up or you could present them with a set of the cards and ask them to find a particular number.

The cards can be used in conjunction with the blank hundred square on Sheet 7. Children can take turns picking a card from this set and writing the number it shows in the correct place on the hundred square. Alternatively, the teacher can pick out individual cards and ask the children to write the numbers on the blank hundred square or on the 0 to 99 square if preferred.

Number Flashcards (2)

55	56	57	58	59
60	61	62	63	64
65	66	67	68	69
70	71	72	73	74
75	76	77	78	79
80	81	82	83	84
85	86	87	88	89
90	91	92	93	94
95	96	97	98	99
100	101	102	103	104
105	106	107	108	109

Bits of the Square

In solving the puzzles on Sheet 10, pupils are using their knowledge of addition, subtraction and place value. We suggest that this sheet is photocopied onto an OHP transparency and used for **oral work and mental calculation**. It can also be copied onto paper for pupils to complete in pairs or individually.

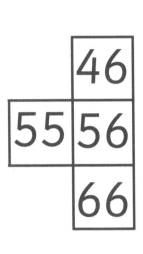

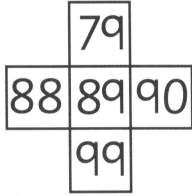

Pupils will observe that the values of numbers go up by 10 as you go down the sheet and up by 1 as you move to the right.

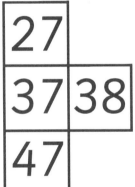

Name: Date:

The puzzles below show parts of a hundred square. Try to remember how the numbers are arranged on a hundred square, then work out what the missing numbers are and fill them in.

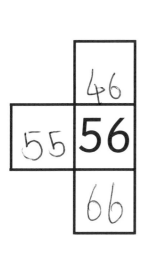

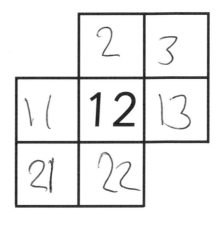

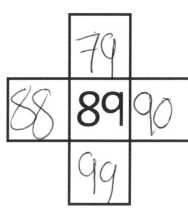

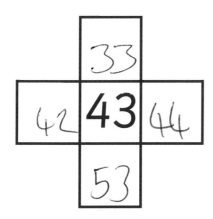

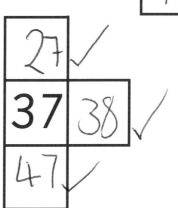

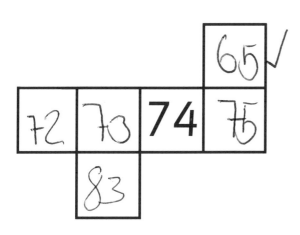

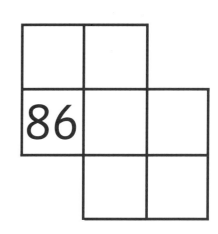

Numbers in Words (1)

Children need to read and write numbers. The National Numeracy Strategy expects Year 1 pupils to read and write numbers to at least 20. Year 2 pupils should read and write numbers to at least 100.

Sheet 11 gives practice in reading and writing numbers up to and including 20.

Special features of spellings can be pointed out:

> ... the matching letter patterns in seven and eleven

> ... the letter pattern teen - some pupils will have brothers and sisters who are 'teenagers': you could discuss why they are called that

> ... the twe in twelve and twenty

> ... the link between numbers such as six and sixteen, discussing the strange links between three and thirteen and five and fifteen

Numbers in Words (1)

Name: Date:

Match the numbers to the words. The first one is done for you.	Write the numbers. The first one is done for you.

Match the numbers to the words. The first one is done for you.

19	eleven
7	eight
13	nineteen
11	seventeen
8	fourteen
17	seven
12	thirteen
14	twelve

19 ─── nineteen

Write the numbers. The first one is done for you.

three	→	3
sixteen	→	
nine	→	
fifteen	→	
ten	→	
eighteen	→	
five	→	
twenty	→	

Write these numbers in words:

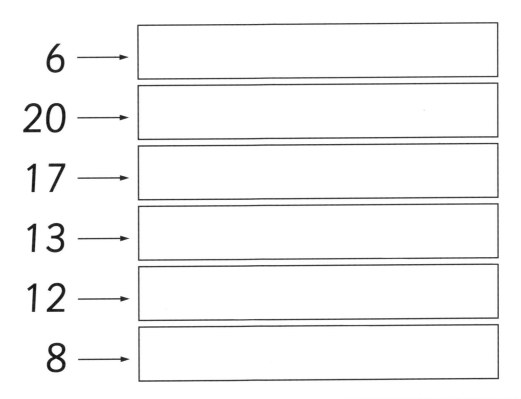

6 →

20 →

17 →

13 →

12 →

8 →

Numbers in Words (2)

Children need to read and write numbers. The National Numeracy Strategy expects Year 1 pupils to read and write numbers to at least 20. Year 2 pupils should read and write numbers to at least 100. The word thousand is also included in the *Mathematical Vocabulary* supplement to the National Numeracy Strategy.

Sheet 12 gives practice in reading and writing numbers up to and including 100. We have not included every number but have ensured that the more difficult ones are featured.

Special features of spellings can be pointed out:

> ... the matching letter patterns in four and fourteen but the fact that there is no u in forty

> ... the links between three, thirteen and thirty

> ... the red in hundred

> ... the sand in thousand

Numbers in Words (2)

Name: Date:

Match the numbers to the words.
The first one is done for you.

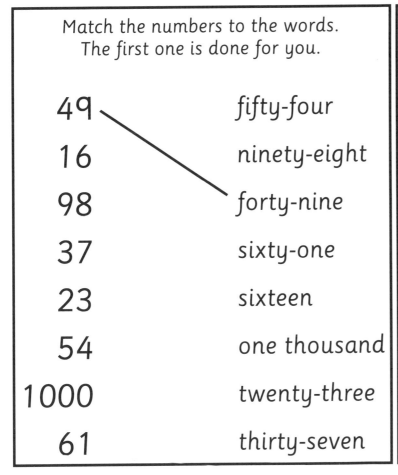

49	fifty-four
16	ninety-eight
98	forty-nine
37	sixty-one
23	sixteen
54	one thousand
1000	twenty-three
61	thirty-seven

Write the numbers.
The first one is done for you.

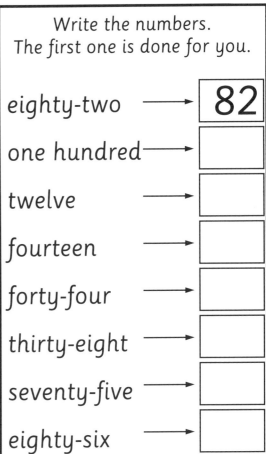

eighty-two → 82
one hundred →
twelve →
fourteen →
forty-four →
thirty-eight →
seventy-five →
eighty-six →

Write these numbers in words:

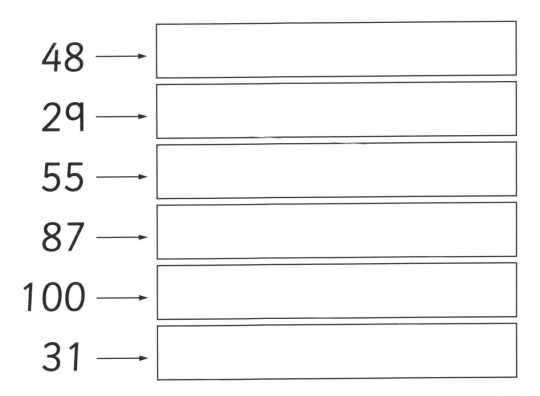

48 →

29 →

55 →

87 →

100 →

31 →

4 x 4 Number Squares

The National Numeracy Strategy suggests that Year 2 pupils should use 4 x 4 number grids. On Sheet 13 we have provided four copies of a 4 x 4 square. You may wish to photocopy this sheet, and Sheets 14 and 15, onto overhead projector transparencies for use during **oral work and mental calculation**. Interesting comparisons can be made between the patterns which are made on each type of square when completing repeated operations.

Repeated operations which you may like to set for the pupils to complete on their own copies of Sheet 13 could include:

… starting at 1 and repeatedly adding 3, colouring in as they go:

1	2	3	4
5	6	7	8
9	10	11	12
13	14	15	16

… starting at 2 and repeatedly adding 3:

1	2	3	4
5	6	7	8
9	10	11	12
13	14	15	16

… starting at 3 and repeatedly adding 3:

1	2	3	4
5	6	7	8
9	10	11	12
13	14	15	16

Now try the same repeated operations on a
5 x 5 square (Sheet 14) or a 6 x 6 square (Sheet 15)

4 x 4 Number Squares

Name: Date:

1	2	3	4
5	6	7	8
9	10	11	12
13	14	15	16

1	2	3	4
5	6	7	8
9	10	11	12
13	14	15	16

1	2	3	4
5	6	7	8
9	10	11	12
13	14	15	16

1	2	3	4
5	6	7	8
9	10	11	12
13	14	15	16

5 x 5 Number Squares

The National Numeracy Strategy suggests that Year 2 pupils should use a 5 x 5 number grid. We have provided two 5 x 5 number grids on Sheet 14.

There are many combinations of activities which pupils can do:

They can start at one and count on in threes, colouring the numbers they arrive at:

1	2	3	4	5
6	7	8	9	10
11	12	13	14	15
16	17	18	19	20
21	22	23	24	25

They could start at two or three and count on in threes.

This square shows the pattern from starting at two: Are the same number of squares covered as when we started at one?

1	2	3	4	5
6	7	8	9	10
11	12	13	14	15
16	17	18	19	20
21	22	23	24	25

They could start at one or two and count on in twos.

This square shows the pattern from starting at two:

1	2	3	4	5
6	7	8	9	10
11	12	13	14	15
16	17	18	19	20
21	22	23	24	25

They could count on in fours.

This square shows the pattern from starting at two:

1	2	3	4	5
6	7	8	9	10
11	12	13	14	15
16	17	18	19	20
21	22	23	24	25

… they could make predictions of what would happen if the square went beyond the number 25 … if, for example, they start at two and count on in fours, would 29 be coloured? … Would 35?

5 x 5 Number Squares

Name: Date:

1	2	3	4	5
6	7	8	9	10
11	12	13	14	15
16	17	18	19	20
21	22	23	24	25

1	2	3	4	5
6	7	8	9	10
11	12	13	14	15
16	17	18	19	20
21	22	23	24	25

6 x 6 Number Squares

The National Numeracy Strategy suggests that Year 2 pupils should use a 6 x 6 number grid. We have provided two copies on Sheet 15.

There are many combinations of activities which pupils can do:

> … they can start at three and count on in threes, colouring the numbers they arrive at

> … they could start at two and count on in threes

> … they could start at one or two and count on in twos

> … they could count on in fours or fives or sixes

> … they could make predictions of what would happen if the square went beyond the number 36 … if, for example, they start at four and count on in fives, would 38 be coloured? … Would 42?

> … they could compare the pattern of threes made on the 5 x 5 square with the 6 x 6 square. If they start on two and count on in threes will they reach the same numbers on both squares? When they see that they will, they could compare the patterns which their colouring of these numbers make.

Remember, every time children see a pattern in numbers their mental skills are being strengthened. It is important for you as a teacher to point out what they have learnt by encouraging them to say the facts observed out loud …

> '… I started at 2 and counted on 3 and I reached 5. 2 add 3 equals 5.
> I kept adding on 3. 5 add 3 equals 8. 8 add 3 equals 11. 11 add 3 equals 14 …'

1	2	3	4	5	6
7	8	9	10	11	12
13	14	15	16	17	18
19	20	21	22	23	24
25	26	27	28	29	30
31	32	33	34	35	36

6 x 6 Number Squares

Name: Date:

1	2	3	4	5	6
7	8	9	10	11	12
13	14	15	16	17	18
19	20	21	22	23	24
25	26	27	28	29	30
31	32	33	34	35	36

1	2	3	4	5	6
7	8	9	10	11	12
13	14	15	16	17	18
19	20	21	22	23	24
25	26	27	28	29	30
31	32	33	34	35	36

The National Numeracy Strategy suggests that Reception and Year 1 pupils should match numbers to dot patterns.

On Sheets 16 and 17 we provide a complete set of dominoes where the dots are not arranged in the traditional domino pattern. Accordingly, children need to count the dots each time to establish how many are there. This gives excellent practice of counting numbers up to six.

The dominoes can be used to play a traditional domino game or variations upon it. We suggest that children work in pairs, sharing out the set completely between them. They then take it in turns to lay a domino where one side of it matches one of the ends of the row of dominoes already placed.

There are alternative uses of the Random Spot Dominoes:

... you could give a copy of Sheet 18, together with six dominoes to each child in a small group: ask them to place the dominoes, one at a time, on the central sections of the sheet, then to write the correct numeral on each side

... you give each child a small set of dominoes and a set of digit cards (showing 1 to 6 only) and ask the child to match the digits to the dominoes, one at a time

... you could give each child a small set of dominoes to count the dots on each side of each domino and produce an addition sentence:

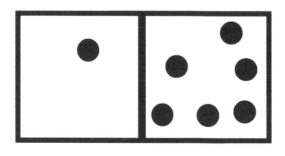

1 + 6 = 7

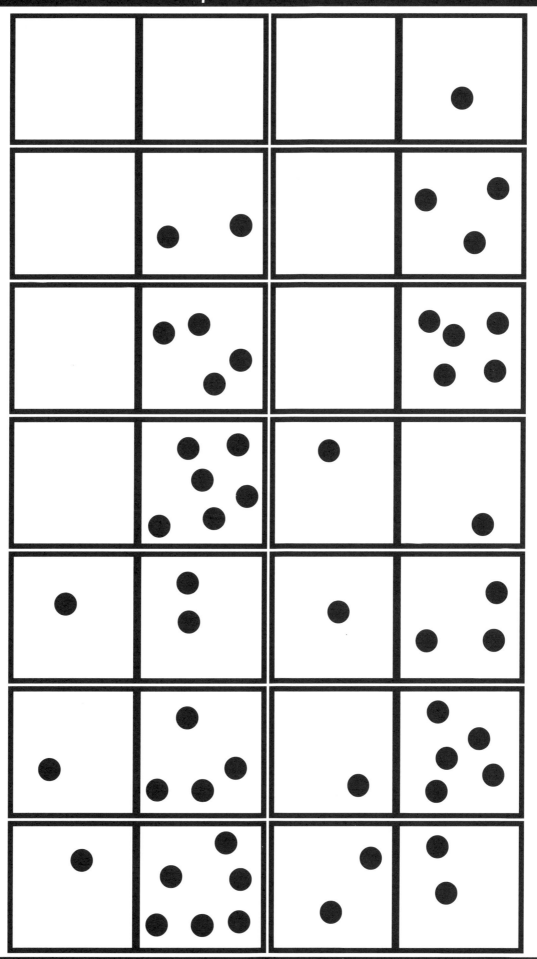

The National Numeracy Strategy suggests that Reception and Year 1 pupils should match numbers to dot patterns.

On Sheets 16 and 17 we provide a complete set of dominoes where the dots are not arranged in the traditional domino pattern. Accordingly, children need to count the dots each time to establish how many are there. This gives excellent practice of counting numbers up to six.

The dominoes can be used to play a traditional domino game or variations upon it. We suggest that children work in pairs, sharing out the set completely between them. They then take it in turns to lay a domino where one side of it matches one of the ends of the row of dominoes already placed.

There are alternative uses of the Random Spot Dominoes:

> ... you could give a copy of Sheet 18, together with six dominoes to each child in a small group: ask them to place the dominoes, one at a time, on the central sections of the sheet, then to write the correct numeral on each side

> ... you give each child a small set of dominoes and a set of digit cards (showing 1 to 6 only) and ask the child to match the digits to the dominoes, one at a time

> ... you could give each child a small set of dominoes to count the dots on each side of each domino and produce an addition sentence:

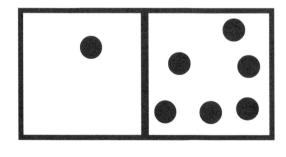

1 + 6 = 7

Random Spot Dominoes (2)

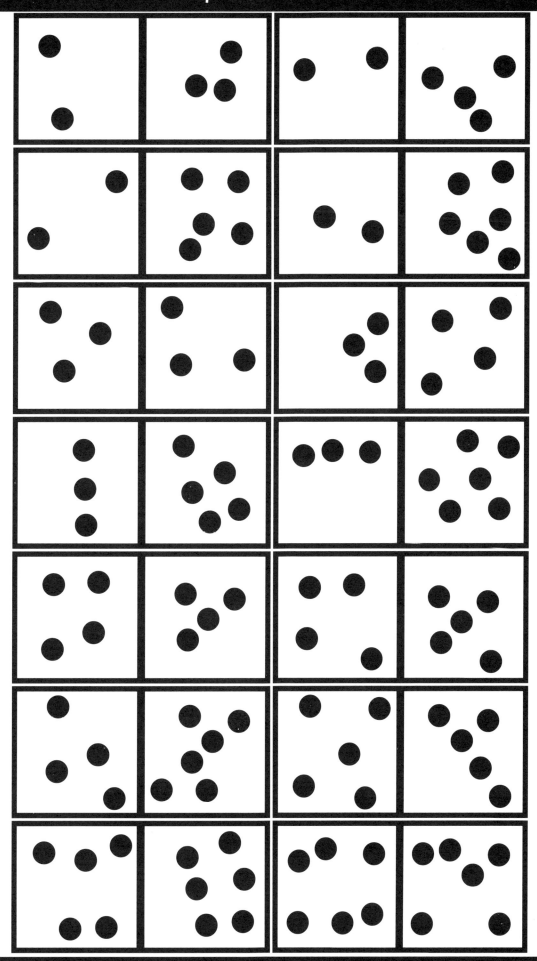

Domino Spot Count

Sheet 18 can be used with the Random Spot Dominoes made from Sheets 16 and 17.

Pupils in Reception or Year 1 need to be able to count confidently, up to ten and beyond. They also need to be able to write the numerals up to 9. Sheet 18 provides an excellent opportunity to practise both skills.

Pupils work individually placing a domino in the top domino space, counting the number of spots on the left side of the domino and writing it in the left box, then counting the number of spots on the right side of the domino and writing it in the right box:

1		6
	Put a domino here.	

They then take another domino, put it in the next space and write the appropriate numbers in the boxes.

As an alternative, you could ask the children to write the number word instead:

one		six
	Put a domino here.	

Domino Spot Count

	Put a domino here.	
	Put a domino here.	
	Put a domino here.	
	Put a domino here.	
	Put a domino here.	
	Put a domino here.	

The National Numeracy Strategy suggests that Year 1 pupils should collect data, then create a visual representation of the data. They can do this by drawing or, for example, by using mathematical linking cubes to create 'towers'. Having represented the data, the children then make simple interpretations of it. Similarly, Year 2 pupils should make simple block graphs from data which they have collected, then interpret the information.

Pupils should be encouraged to seek information within the class or at home to be able to gather data and create mathematical representations of it. A simple question such as 'do you prefer hot drinks or cold drinks?' could be a good starting point as the data would produce a block graph of just two columns. This makes it easy for the pupils to see that:

...the total number of people who replied to the question can be found by adding the numbers represented by the two columns;

...the most popular choice is represented by the tallest column;

...the question 'how many more people chose .....?' can be answered by finding the difference between the heights of the two columns.

On Sheet 19 we present a block graph showing information which has already been gathered and which pupils can now interpret.

For speed of marking the answers are as follows:

Potatoes are the most popular vegetable.
Beans are the least popular vegetable.
Two more people prefer peas to beans.
There are 21 people in the class.

You could ask pupils to write the vegetables in order of popularity:

Potatoes, carrots, peas, beans.

Pupils in your class could gather data asking the same question: 'Which is your favourite vegetable out of carrots, potatoes, beans and peas?' Do your children find that potatoes are most popular and beans are least popular? Do they find the same order of popularity?

Data Handling: Block Graph

Name: Date:

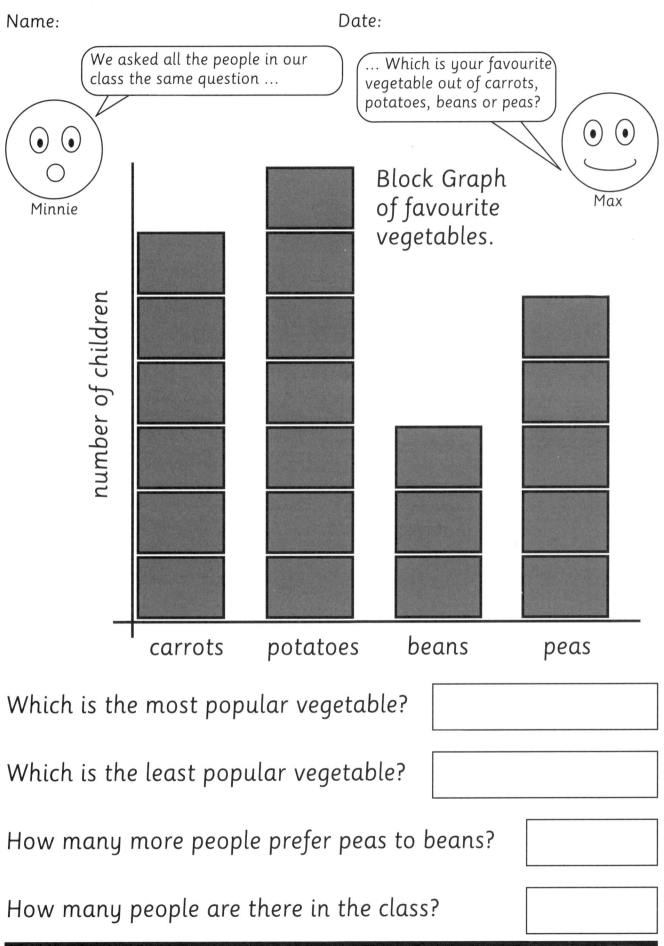

Which is the most popular vegetable?

Which is the least popular vegetable?

How many more people prefer peas to beans?

How many people are there in the class?

Data Handling: Pictogram

The National Numeracy Strategy suggests that Year 2 pupils should collect data, then create simple pictograms where the symbol used represents one unit. Having represented the data, the children then make simple interpretations of it.

Pupils should be encouraged to seek information within the class or at home to be able to gather data and create mathematical representations of it. A simple question such as 'do you prefer tea or coffee?' could be a good starting point. This makes it easy for the pupils to see that:

> …the total number of people who replied to the question can be found by adding the numbers represented by the two columns or rows of pictures;

> …the most popular choice is represented by the tallest column or longest row;

> …the question 'how many more people chose .....?' can be answered by finding the difference between the heights of the columns or the lengths of the rows.

On Sheet 20 we present a pictogram showing information which has already been gathered and which pupils can now interpret. We have arranged the information in rows rather than columns though pictograms can be represented in either way.

For speed of marking the answers are as follows:

> Coffee is the most popular drink.
> Hot chocolate is the least popular drink.
> Fourteen people have hot drinks.
> Three people have cold drinks.

You could ask pupils how many adults are shown on the pictogram altogether.

Pupils in your school could gather data asking the same question to the adults:

> 'What drink do you have at breaktime?'

Do your children find similar results to those found by Max and Minnie?

Data Handling: Pictogram

Name: Date:

Minnie: We asked all the adults in our school the same question ...

Max: ... What drink do you have at breaktime?

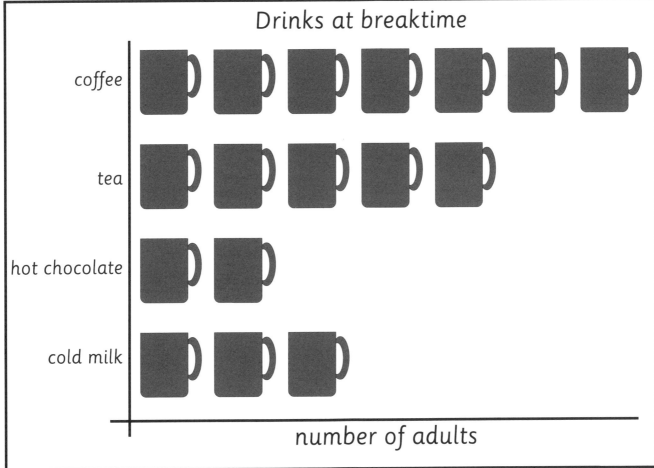

Drinks at breaktime

coffee

tea

hot chocolate

cold milk

number of adults

Which is the most popular drink?

Which is the least popular drink?

How many people have hot drinks?

How many people have cold drinks?

Bond Cards - Addition to 6

The National Numeracy Strategy suggests that teachers should have bundles of cards showing addition and subtraction bonds.

Sheet 21 contains all the addition bonds which have a total of 1, 2, 3, 4, 5 or 6. Year 1 pupils are required to know all the addition bonds up to 5 and Year 2 pupils need to know all the addition bonds to 10. They also need to know the corresponding subtraction facts - these are shown on Sheets 23, 24 and 25.

Addition bonds to 7, 8 and 9 are provided on Sheet 22 and the addition and subtraction bonds of 10 are provided on Sheet 23.

We suggest that the sheet is photocopied onto card and laminated, if possible, before being cut into individual cards. We have arranged the cards for ease of slicing with a paper cutter.

The cards can be used with the number cards from Sheet 1. You could, for example, give each child in a group a different number card and then ask them to find all the addition bond cards which match the card they have.

During your **oral work and mental calculation** time, you could pick out Bond Cards at random for pupils to work out the answer. With repeated practice they will be able to rely on their memories for rapid recall of the answers. This is the ultimate aim.

0 + 1	1 + 0	0 + 2
2 + 0	1 + 1	0 + 3
3 + 0	1 + 2	2 + 1
0 + 4	4 + 0	1 + 3
3 + 1	2 + 2	0 + 5
5 + 0	1 + 4	4 + 1
2 + 3	3 + 2	0 + 6
6 + 0	1 + 5	5 + 1
2 + 4	4 + 2	3 + 3

The National Numeracy Strategy suggests that teachers should have bundles of cards showing addition and subtraction bonds.

Sheet 22 contains all the addition bonds with totals of 7, 8 or 9. Pupils also need to know the corresponding subtraction facts - these are shown on Sheets 24 and 25.

Year 2 pupils need to know all the addition bonds to 10. Addition and subtraction bonds of 10 are provided on Sheet 23.

We suggest that the sheet is photocopied onto card and laminated, if possible, before being cut into individual cards. We have arranged the cards for ease of slicing with a paper cutter.

The cards can be used with the number cards from Sheet 1. You could, for example, give each child in a group a different number card and then ask them to find all the addition bond cards which match the card they have.

During your **oral work and mental calculation** time, you could pick out Bond Cards at random for pupils to work out the answer. With repeated practice they will be able to rely on their memories for rapid recall of the answers. This is the ultimate aim.

A valuable activity is to give two pupils the complete set of cards and to ask them to find pairs of cards which are worth the same.

They could create number sentences such as: $6 + 2 = 7 + 1$

You could ask the pupils to put the cards into two piles then to pick a card from each pile and place them on the table. They then have to choose the appropriate card (cut from Sheet 2) to show the relationship between the two cards on the table: ie =, < or >.

For example: $5 + 3 > 1 + 6$

0 + 7	7 + 0	1 + 6
6 + 1	2 + 5	5 + 2
3 + 4	4 + 3	0 + 8
8 + 0	1 + 7	7 + 1
2 + 6	6 + 2	3 + 5
5 + 3	4 + 4	0 + 9
9 + 0	1 + 8	8 + 1
2 + 7	7 + 2	3 + 6
6 + 3	4 + 5	5 + 4

Bonds of 10

The National Numeracy Strategy suggests that teachers should have bundles of cards showing addition and subtraction bonds.

Sheet 23 contains all the addition bonds with totals of 10, then the subtraction from 10 bonds. Year 2 pupils should know all of these. We have also included two multiplication facts with a product of 10, together with three other ways of making 10.

We suggest that the sheet is photocopied onto card and laminated, if possible, before being cut into individual cards. We have arranged the cards for ease of slicing with a paper cutter.

During your **oral work and mental calculation** time, you could pick out Bond Cards at random for pupils to work out the answer. With repeated practice they will be able to rely on their memories for rapid recall of the answers. This is the ultimate aim.

Bonds of 10

0 + 10	10 + 0	1 + 9
9 + 1	2 + 8	8 + 2
3 + 7	7 + 3	4 + 6
6 + 4	5 + 5	10 – 0
10 – 1	10 – 2	10 – 3
10 – 4	10 – 5	10 – 6
10 – 7	10 – 8	10 – 9
10 – 10	5 x 2	2 x 5
20 – 10	Double five	Half of twenty

The National Numeracy Strategy suggests that teachers should have bundles of cards showing addition and subtraction bonds.

Sheet 24 contains all the subtraction bonds from 9, 8 and 7. Year 2 pupils need to know all of these.

We suggest that the sheet is photocopied onto card and laminated, if possible, before being cut into individual cards. We have arranged the cards for ease of slicing with a paper cutter.

The cards can be used with the number cards from Sheet 1. You could, for example, give each child in a group a different number card and then ask them to find all the subtraction bond cards which match the card they have.

During your **oral work and mental calculation** time, you could pick out Bond Cards at random for pupils to work out the answer. With repeated practice they will be able to rely on their memories for rapid recall of the answers.

A valuable activity is to give two pupils the complete set of cards and to ask them to find pairs of cards which are worth the same.

They could create number sentences such as: $9 - 2 = 8 - 1$

You could ask the pupils to put the cards into two piles then to pick a card from each pile and place them on the table. They then have to choose the appropriate card (cut from Sheet 2) to show the relationship between the two cards on the table: ie =, < or >.

For example: $7 - 4 < 8 - 1$

9 – 9	9 – 8	9 – 7
9 – 6	9 – 5	9 – 4
9 – 3	9 – 2	9 – 1
9 – 0	8 – 8	8 – 7
8 – 6	8 – 5	8 – 4
8 – 3	8 – 2	8 – 1
8 – 0	7 – 7	7 – 6
7 – 5	7 – 4	7 – 3
7 – 2	7 – 1	7 – 0

The National Numeracy Strategy suggests that teachers should have bundles of cards showing addition and subtraction bonds.

Sheet 25 contains all the subtraction bonds from 6, 5, 4, 3, 2 and 1. Year 2 pupils need to know all of these. Year 1 pupils need to know all the subtraction bonds from 5, 4, 3, 2 and 1.

We suggest that the sheet is photocopied onto card and laminated, if possible, before being cut into individual cards. We have arranged the cards for ease of slicing with a paper cutter.

The cards can be used with the number cards from Sheet 1. You could, for example, give each child in a group a different number card and then ask them to find all the subtraction bond cards which match the card they have.

During your **oral work and mental calculation** time, you could pick out Bond Cards at random for pupils to work out the answer. With repeated practice they will be able to rely on their memories for rapid recall of the answers.

A valuable activity is to give two pupils the complete set of cards and to ask them to find pairs of cards which are worth the same.

They could create number sentences such as: $6 - 2 = 5 - 1$

You could ask the pupils to put the cards into two piles then to pick a card from each pile and place them on the table. They then have to choose the appropriate card (cut from Sheet 2) to show the relationship between the two cards on the table: ie $=$, $<$ or $>$.

For example: $5 - 1 > 6 - 4$

6 – 6	6 – 5	6 – 4
6 – 3	6 – 2	6 – 1
6 – 0	5 – 5	5 – 4
5 – 3	5 – 2	5 – 1
5 – 0	4 – 4	4 – 3
4 – 2	4 – 1	4 – 0
3 – 3	3 – 2	3 – 1
3 – 0	2 – 2	2 – 1
2 – 0	1 – 1	1 – 0

Bonds of 20 (1)

The National Numeracy Strategy suggests that teachers should have bundles of cards showing addition and subtraction bonds.

Sheet 26 contains all the addition bonds with totals of 20, which Year 2 pupils should know by heart. We have also included four multiplication facts with a product of 20, together with two other ways of making 20.

We suggest that the sheet is photocopied onto card and laminated, if possible, before being cut into individual cards. We have arranged the cards for ease of slicing with a paper cutter.

During your **oral work and mental calculation** time, you could pick out Bond Cards at random for pupils to work out the answer. As all the answers to this sheet are 20, you would need to mix these cards with other Bond Cards so that these will come up at random. Regular practice will ensure that children acquire a thorough knowledge of addition facts so that ultimately they can produce answers 'automatically'.

Alternatively, you could ask the children to write down as many ways they can think of to make a total of 20. You could then show them this whole sheet for checking their answers, pointing out, of course, that the bottom six cards are not additions.

Bonds of 20 (1)

0 + 20	20 + 0	1 + 19
19 + 1	2 + 18	18 + 2
3 + 17	17 + 3	4 + 16
16 + 4	5 + 15	15 + 5
6 + 14	14 + 6	7 + 13
13 + 7	8 + 12	12 + 8
9 + 11	11 + 9	10 + 10
5 x 4	4 x 5	2 x 10
10 x 2	Double ten	Half of forty

Bonds of 20 (2)

The National Numeracy Strategy suggests that teachers should have bundles of cards showing addition and subtraction bonds.

Sheet 27 contains all the subtraction bonds from 20, which Year 2 pupils should know by heart. We have also included six cards which you can use as flashcards, asking the children to 'make 20' for each one. These six cards represent an important aspect of numeracy. The use of the box symbol to represent a missing number is the first stage in algebra work. Sheet 28 features a further collection of this type of card.

During your **oral work and mental calculation** time, you could pick out Bond Cards at random for pupils to work out the answer. Regular practice will ensure that children acquire a thorough knowledge of addition facts so that ultimately they can produce answers 'automatically'.

Bonds of 20 (2)

20 – 0	20 – 1	20 – 2
20 – 3	20 – 4	20 – 5
20 – 6	20 – 7	20 – 8
20 – 9	20 – 10	20 – 11
20 – 12	20 – 13	20 – 14
20 – 15	20 – 16	20 – 17
20 – 18	20 – 19	20 – 20
15 + ☐	16 + ☐	17 + ☐
18 + ☐	19 + ☐	20 + ☐

Bonds: Target Setting

Sheet 28 features a set of flashcards which represent an important aspect of numeracy. The use of the box symbol to represent a missing number is the first stage in algebra work.

We suggest that you use these cards regularly as part of your **oral work and mental calculation** session. You could use the cards every day for a week, each day setting a new target.

For example, you could set the target as 5. You would need to use this set of cards:

$1 + \square$, $2 + \square$, $3 + \square$, $4 + \square$, $5 + \square$, $\square + 1$, $\square + 2$, $\square + 3$, $\square + 4$, $\square + 5$

… as these cards can all potentially have a total of 5.
 It is very important not to include any of the other cards as these cannot have a total of 5 - we do not want to introduce negative numbers at this stage. The children have to work out the missing number as quickly as possible then put their hands up to offer their answer. The activity can be more fun if the children are encouraged to respond quickly.

The next day you could include these cards: $6 + \square$, $7 + \square$, $\square + 6$, $\square + 7$ as well as the cards you used the day before, setting a new target total of 7.

Each day you would change the target, making sure that you had the appropriate set of cards for the target chosen. After one week you could stop, then have a week's break, then start the daily activity again.

The final card, $\square + \triangle$, can be used with any target.

Bonds: Target Setting

1 + ☐	2 + ☐	3 + ☐
4 + ☐	5 + ☐	6 + ☐
7 + ☐	8 + ☐	9 + ☐
10 + ☐	11 + ☐	12 + ☐
13 + ☐	14 + ☐	☐ + 1
☐ + 2	☐ + 3	☐ + 4
☐ + 5	☐ + 6	☐ + 7
☐ + 8	☐ + 9	☐ + 10
☐ + 11	☐ + 12	☐ + △

Bonds of 100

Year 2 pupils need to know all the pairs of multiples of 10 that have a total of 100. On Sheet 29 we have featured cards with 'missing number boxes' so that children can be set the challenge of making 100. The first cards on the sheet are also designed to provide practice in finding the pairs of multiples which make 100.

We suggest that the sheet is photocopied onto card and laminated, if possible, before being cut into individual cards. We have arranged the cards for ease of slicing with a paper cutter.

During your oral work and mental calculation time, you could pick out Bond Cards at random for pupils to work out the answer. With repeated practice they will be able to rely on their memories for rapid recall of the answers. This is the ultimate aim.

Bonds of 100

100 – 0	100 – 10	100 – 20
100 – 30	100 – 40	100 – 50
100 – 60	100 – 70	100 – 80
100 – 90	100 – 100	☐ + 90
☐ + 80	☐ + 70	☐ + 60
☐ + 50	☐ + 40	☐ + 30
☐ + 20	☐ + 10	☐ + 0
10 + ☐	20 + ☐	40 + ☐
60 + ☐	80 + ☐	Double fifty

Counting (1)

Sheet 30 is designed to be photocopied onto an overhead projector transparency for use during an **oral work and mental calculation** session with Reception children. We recommend that you use the three sets of pictures to count together with the pupils.

If you have access to an overhead projector, you can cover the rings and cars pictures while talking about the bears. You could ask a volunteer to count while others watch. Use counters to place on each bear as you count. Now count the bears without the counters, pointing to each one as you count. 'Now try counting without pointing.'

You can count the rings and the cars in a similar way. As an extension, you might like to discuss the directions the cars are facing: 'Four cars are facing to the left, two cars are facing to the right, there are six cars altogether.'

If you don't have use of an overhead projector in class, the sheet could be enlarged, then copied onto paper or card and used for the focus of a discussion in much the same way as with an OHP.

The sheet can also be copied onto paper and given to pupils to complete individually or in pairs. The children can count the objects then enter the number in the answer boxes before colouring in the pictures.

Name:

 How many
bears are there?

How many
rings are there?

 How many
cars are there?

Counting (2)

The set of fish bowls on Sheet 31 are designed to be considered by Reception or Year 1 pupils. Children counting the fish in the bowls are beyond the earliest stages of counting as they will now be developing strategies for counting objects which are not regularly spaced or neatly laid out. Some of the fish overlap, for example. Notice as well that we have asked the question, 'How many fish *can you see* in each bowl?' The possibility that some fish may be hidden behind others could be discussed with more advanced children.

We have deliberately shown an empty bowl. The concept of 'none' , represented by 'zero' needs to be discussed with the children.

There are other opportunities for discussion during your **oral work and mental calculation** session. You could ask:

… Which two bowls have the same number of fish?

… Which bowl has the most fish in?

… How many fish are swimming towards the left in this bowl?

… How many fish are swimming towards the right in this bowl?

Having seen how many fish are swimming in each direction in a particular bowl, you could stress the number bond which the picture illustrates. For example, the bowl where two fish are swimming towards the right and three fish are swimming towards the left illustrates the bonds $2 + 3 = 5$ or $3 + 2 = 5$.

Counting (2)

Name: Date:

How many fish can you see in each bowl?

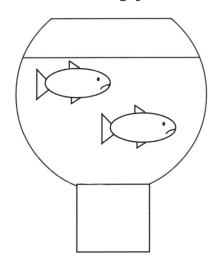
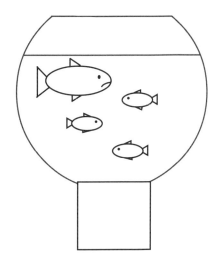
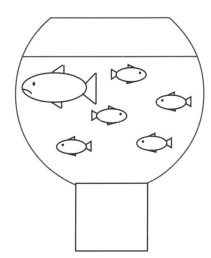

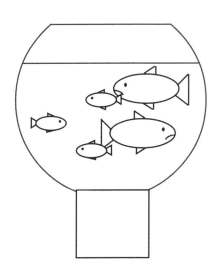
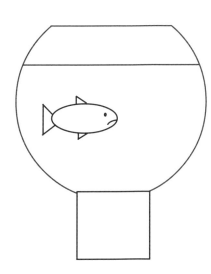
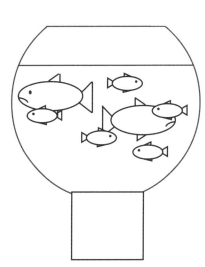

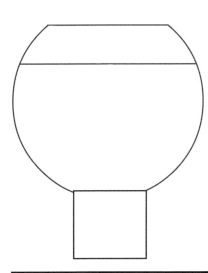
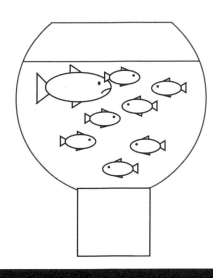
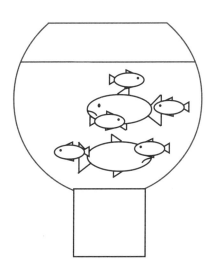

Counting (3)

Sheet 32 can be used during **oral work and mental calculation** with pupils in Reception, Year 1 or Year 2, for counting together to larger numbers. Year 2 pupils need to count large collections of objects by grouping them in tens, fives or twos. This can be done most valuably by counting physical objects such as buttons, nuts, leaves, shells, etc. However, it is sometimes necessary to count objects which cannot be physically picked up and moved.

On Sheet 32 we have provided three large sets of objects in pictures. The pupils can adopt various methods for counting them. They could place a physical object such as a unit cube onto each pictured object. They can simply count by pointing with their fingers. They can draw rings around sets of five or ten, then count up 5, 10, 15, etc or 10, 20, 30, etc, adding on the remaining ones at the end.

We recommend that you ask the children to make an estimate of the number of objects in each set before employing one of the counting methods.

'How close was your estimate?'

'Did everybody count in the same way?'

'Did everybody get the same answer?'

'If not we could count again.'

The sheet can be used as the focus for much discussion. You could, for example, ask the children how many large fish and how many small fish there are, then how many fish altogether. You could write a number sentence in relation to this: $12 + 21 = 33$.

You could ask the children to estimate how many cats and how many rabbits there are. 'Do you think there are the same number of cats and rabbits?' Count the cats together and count the rabbits together. Now count all the animals together. Create the number sentence: $11 + 11 = 22$. Discuss 'double eleven makes twenty-two.' Go on to discussing other doubles.

The actual answers are: 25 motorbikes (11 facing to the right, 14 to the left)

33 fish (12 large, 21 small)

22 animals (11 cats and 11 rabbits)

Counting (3)

Name: Date:

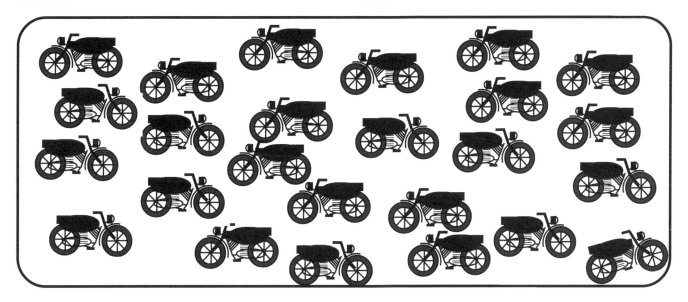

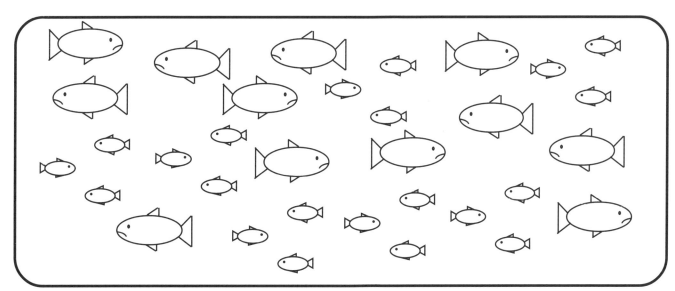

Numbers in Sequence

Sheet 33 provides two dot-to-dot pictures for use by pupils in Reception or Year 1. Reception pupils need to recognise numerals, firstly from 1 to 9, then 0 and 10, then beyond 10. Year 1 pupils need to be able to read and write numbers to at least 20. Children will have lots of practice in working with number lines during your oral work and mental calculation times. Our dot-to-dot pictures will give some reinforcement of this work, especially as the numbers are scattered rather than arranged in a neat line as on a number track.

We suggest that you introduce the activity to a group then leave them to complete the pictures by joining the dots with 'straight' lines. They can add further details to the pictures themselves.

Numbers in Sequence

Name: Date:

4   5

3

2   6

14   13   10   9

1   7
16 15   12   11   8

4 5
2   3 6   7

1
12   9 8

11   10

Numbers Game

Sheet 34 features a set of numbers, 1 to 9.

For Reception children, the task is simply to point to the numbers in the correct sequence. We suggest that you photocopy the sheet onto an overhead projector transparency or onto paper or card for use during **oral work and mental calculation**. Children take it in turns to point to the numbers, saying '1, 2, 3, 4, 5, 6, 7, 8, 9', as they do so. Some children will be able to gain speed in the activity. The sheet could be used on several occasions but you should avoid over-familiarity as some children will begin to think that numbers are always arranged in this way!

For Year 1 children we suggest that the sheet is copied onto paper or card, then laminated or put inside a plastic wallet. The children work in pairs to take part in a simple number bonds game. Each child stands with the sheet on the floor at about one metre in front of them, then throws, gently, two pennies onto the card, adding together whichever two numbers the coins land on - the number is awarded simply by the penny touching the particular number's square. To avoid argument, we have arranged the numbers into squares in such a way that a penny can only ever touch one square. The next person takes a turn and adds together their two numbers. Whoever has the highest score wins that round. Now they start again.

Year 2 children can work in a similar way to Year 1 but they can extend their activity by keeping a cumulative score by only dropping one penny at a time. They record their own scores, adding on each time they have a turn. You can decide the winning target: for example, the winner could be the first to reach a total of 50 or more, or a total of 100 or more. An alternative version is to give a starting figure of 50 or 100; on each turn the pupil subtracts their score. The winner then is the first person to get to zero.

6	1	7
3	q	5
8	4	2

Number Track (1)

The number track on Sheet 35 needs to be combined with the 50 to 100 section on Sheet 36. It is designed to be copied onto paper or card then cut into strips. We have repeated each ten so that the strips can be overlapped and glued together to make a continuous track from 0 to 100. This should be fastened to the wall, fixed with staples fired vertically **exactly** along some of the vertical lines between the numbers and fired horizontally along the bottom edge.

You may like to have several copies of the track on your classroom walls for pupils to refer to.

The number track has many uses throughout the primary school:

… you could ask the children to start on the number 7 and jump 4 to 11, then to start on 17 and jump 4, then start on 27 and jump 4. Do they notice that adding a 4 to a number with a units value of 7 always produces an answer with a units value of 1? Try the same thing with jumps of 8 or 6 or 9, etc.

… you could ask them to start on 6 and to keep making jumps of 5. Do they notice that the units value keeps alternating between 6 and 1?

… you could ask them to start on 2 and keep jumping in twos. Do they notice that the answers are always even numbers?

… you could ask them to start on 1 and keep jumping in twos. Do they notice that the answers are always odd numbers?

… you could ask them to start on 31 and make jumps of specific numbers backwards.

There are many other examples where patterns can be found. Number tracks and lines often help children to see patterns which they can transfer into their mental work.

The 'leapfrog' cards on Sheets 39 and 40 are designed to be used with the Number Track on Sheets 35 and 36. A leapfrog is slid into position at a specified number on the track (3, for example). You can then ask a child to 'hop' the leapfrog forward a specified number of places (5, for example). Where does the leapfrog land?

3 + 5 = 8

Please see Sheet 39 for further suggestions regarding the use of the number track.

0	1	2	3	4	5	6	7	8	9	10
10	11	12	13	14	15	16	17	18	19	20
20	21	22	23	24	25	26	27	28	29	30
30	31	32	33	34	35	36	37	38	39	40
40	41	42	43	44	45	46	47	48	49	50

Number Track (2)

The number track on Sheet 36 needs to be combined with the 0 to 50 section on Sheet 35. It is designed to be copied onto paper or card then cut into strips. We have repeated each ten so that the strips can be overlapped and glued together to make a continuous track from 0 to 100. This should be fastened to the wall, fixed with staples fired vertically **exactly** along some of the vertical lines between the numbers and fired horizontally along the bottom edge.

You may like to have several copies of the track on your classroom walls for pupils to refer to.

The number track has many uses throughout the primary school:

… you could ask the children to start on the number 7 and jump 4 to 11, then to start on 17 and jump 4, then start on 27 and jump 4. Do they notice that adding a 4 to a number with a units value of 7 always produces an answer with a units value of 1? Try the same thing with jumps of 8 or 6 or 9, etc.

… you could ask them to start on 6 and to keep making jumps of 5. Do they notice that the units value keeps alternating between 6 and 1?

… you could ask them to start on 2 and keep jumping in twos. Do they notice that the answers are always even numbers?

… you could ask them to start on 1 and keep jumping in twos. Do they notice that the answers are always odd numbers?

… you could ask them to start on 82 and make jumps of specific numbers backwards.

There are many other examples where patterns can be found. Number tracks and lines often help children to see patterns which they can transfer into their mental work.

The 'leapfrog' cards on Sheets 39 and 40 are designed to be used with the Number Track on Sheets 35 and 36. A leapfrog is slid into position at a specified number on the track (3, for example). You can then ask a child to 'hop' the leapfrog forward a specified number of places (5, for example). Where does the leapfrog land?

3 + 5 = 8

Please see Sheet 39 for further suggestions regarding the use of the number track.

50	60	70	80	90
51	61	71	81	91
52	62	72	82	92
53	63	73	83	93
54	64	74	84	94
55	65	75	85	95
56	66	76	86	96
57	67	77	87	97
58	68	78	88	98
59	69	79	89	99
60	70	80	90	100

Number Track (3)

The number track on Sheet 37 needs to be combined with the 50 to 100 section on Sheet 38. It is designed to be copied onto paper or card then cut into strips. We have repeated each ten so that the strips can be overlapped and glued together to make a continuous track from 0 to 100. This should be fastened to the wall, fixed with staples fired vertically **exactly** along some of the vertical lines between the numbers and fired horizontally along the bottom edge.

You may like to have several copies of the track on your classroom walls for pupils to refer to.

This number track has blank spaces apart from the multiples of 10. It provides a clear way to practise the multiples of 10. It is also very useful for number awareness. For example:

...where would 25 go on this number track?

...Where would 43 be?

...What number ought to go in the space just before 30?

...What number ought to go in the space just before 50?

The number cards on Sheets 39 and 40 are designed to be used with the Number Track on Sheets 37 and 38. You can ask the children to slide the number cards into specified positions on the Number Track. For example, you could ask one child to place the 6 card in the correct position, another child to place the 15 card, etc:

Please see Sheet 39 for further suggestions regarding the use of the number track.

10	20	30	40	50
10	10	20	30	40

Number Track (4)

The number track on Sheet 38 needs to be combined with the 0 to 50 section on Sheet 37. It is designed to be copied onto paper or card then cut into strips. We have repeated each ten so that the strips can be overlapped and glued together to make a continuous track from 0 to 100. This should be fastened to the wall, fixed with staples fired vertically **exactly** along some of the vertical lines between the numbers and fired horizontally along the bottom edge.

You may like to have several copies of the track on your classroom walls for pupils to refer to.

This number track has blank spaces apart from the multiples of 10. It provides a clear way to practise the multiples of 10. It is also very useful for number awareness. For example:

...where would 65 go on this number track?

...Where would 81 be?

...What number ought to go in the space just before 90?

...What number ought to go in the space just before 100?

The number cards on Sheets 39 and 40 are designed to be used with the Number Track on Sheets 37 and 38. You can ask the children to slide the number cards into specified positions on the Number Track. For example, you could ask one child to place the 6 card in the correct position, another child to place the 15 card, etc:

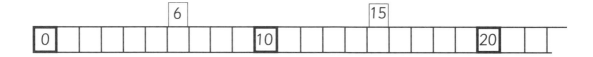

Please see Sheet 39 for further suggestions regarding the use of the number track.

50									60
60									70
70									80
80									90
90									100

Leapfrogs and Numbers (1)

Sheet 39 contains nine copies of our 'leapfrogs', together with numbers from 1 to 49 excluding all tens. Sheet 40 contains the numbers from 51 to 99. The sheets should be photocopied onto card, then cut into small cards by slicing with a paper cutter.

The leapfrogs are designed to be used with the number track on Sheets 35 and 36. The number track should be fastened to the wall with staples along the bottom edge, then with staples exactly along some of the vertical lines between the numbers. You will then find that the leapfrog cards can be slid into position at any number along the track. The children can be asked to complete activities such as:

… 'start at 2, make the leapfrog jump along three numbers. What number has she got to?'

… 'start at 2, make the leapfrog jump in twos. What numbers does she visit?' (You may wish to limit the number of jumps!)

… 'start at 10, make the leapfrog jump two tens forwards. What number has she got to?'

… 'start at 20, make the leapfrog jump three numbers backwards. What number has she got to?'

The number cards are designed to be used with the tens only number track on Sheets 37 and 38:

… a group of children can share the cards out randomly between them, then take turns to slide them into the correct positions along the number track. This provides excellent practice of number awareness.

… you could select the set of multiples of 5 and ask the children to place these in the correct positions along the track.

… you could ask the children to place all the even numbers along the track.

… you could ask the children to place all the odd numbers along the track.

… you could place a number in position, 18 for example, and ask the pupils to keep adding 10, placing all the answers in the correct positions.

1	2	3	4	5	6	7	8	9
11	12	13	14	15	16	17	18	19
21	22	23	24	25	26	27	28	29
31	32	33	34	35	36	37	38	39
41	42	43	44	45	46	47	48	49

Leapfrogs and Numbers (2)

Sheet 40 contains nine copies of our 'leapfrogs', together with numbers from 51 to 99 excluding all tens. Sheets 39 and 40 should be photocopied onto card, then cut into small cards by slicing with a paper cutter.

The leapfrogs are designed to be used with the number track on Sheets 35 and 36. The number track should be fastened to the wall with staples along the bottom edge, then with staples exactly along some of the vertical lines between the numbers. You will then find that the leapfrog cards can be slid into position at any number along the track. The children can be asked to complete activities such as:

… 'start at 2, make the leapfrog jump along three numbers. What number has she got to?'

… 'start at 2, make the leapfrog jump in twos. What numbers does she visit?' (You may wish to limit the number of jumps!)

… 'start at 10, make the leapfrog jump two tens forwards. What number has she got to?'

… 'start at 20, make the leapfrog jump three numbers backwards. What number has she got to?'

The number cards are designed to be used with the tens only number track on Sheets 37 and 38:

… a group of children can share the cards out randomly between them, then take turns to slide them into the correct positions along the number track. This provides excellent practice of number awareness.

… you could select the set of multiples of 5 and ask the children to place these in the correct positions along the track.

… you could ask the children to place all the even numbers along the track.

… you could ask the children to place all the odd numbers along the track.

… you could place a number in position, 18 for example, and ask the pupils to keep adding 10, placing all the answers in the correct positions.

Leapfrogs and Numbers (2)

51	52	53	54	55	56	57	58	59
61	62	63	64	65	66	67	68	69
71	72	73	74	75	76	77	78	79
81	82	83	84	85	86	87	88	89
91	92	93	94	95	96	97	98	99

Shapes (1)

The National Numeracy Strategy indicates that Reception and Year 1 pupils should know the names of the two-dimensional shapes shown on Sheet 41 as part of their mathematical vocabulary: square, rectangle, triangle, circle and star.

Ideally, Sheet 41 should be copied onto an overhead projector transparency and used as the focus for discussion during your **oral work and mental calculation** time.

You could ask children to:

> … point to a shape which has four sides of the same length.
>> 'What is this shape called?'

> … point to a round shape.
>> 'What is this shape called?'

> … point to a shape which has three sides and three corners.
>> 'What is this shape called?'

> … choose a shape on the sheet and describe it to everybody.

Shapes (1)

Name: Date:

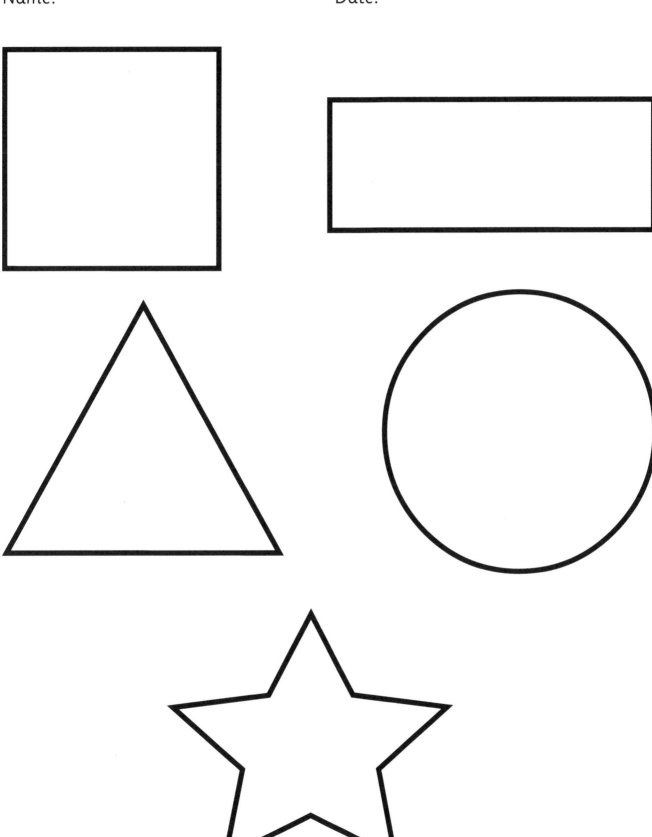

Shapes (2)

The National Numeracy Strategy indicates that Reception and Year 1 pupils should know the names of the two-dimensional shapes shown on Sheet 42 as part of their mathematical vocabulary: square, rectangle, triangle, circle and star.

Sheet 42 is designed as an individual worksheet on which pupils are required to identify specific shapes. The children will need to understand that shapes can be different sizes: for example, a square is still a square whatever its size. They will also need to see that a triangle has three sides but that these don't always need to be equal in size.

You could take the opportunity to use the pictures of the shapes for counting:

... how many triangles are there?

... how many squares are there?

... how many circles are there?

... how many rectangles are there?

... how many stars are there?

... how many four-sided shapes are there?

... how many shapes are there altogether?

Name: Date:

Colour the circles blue.

Colour the triangles green.

Colour the rectangles red.

Colour the squares yellow.

Colour the stars orange.

Shapes (3)

The National Numeracy Strategy indicates that Year 2 pupils should know the names of the two-dimensional shapes shown on Sheet 43 as part of their mathematical vocabulary: square, rectangle, triangle, circle, star, pentagon, hexagon and octagon. Note that triangles, pentagons, hexagons and octagons do not need to have equal sides and equal corners. On Sheet 43 we have shown at least one of each shape which is regular but they do not *have* to be regular.

Ideally, Sheet 43 should be copied onto an overhead projector transparency and used as the focus for discussion during your **oral work and mental calculation** time.

You could ask children to:

 … point to a shape which has four sides of the same length.
  'What is this shape called?'

 … point to a round shape.
  'What is this shape called?'

 … point to a shape which has three sides and three corners.
  'What is this shape called?'

 … point to a shape which has five sides.
  'How many corners has it got?'
  'What is this shape called?'

 … point to a shape which has six sides.
  'How many corners has it got?'
  'What is this shape called?'

 … point to a shape which has eight sides.
  'How many corners has it got?'
  'What is this shape called?'

 … choose a shape on the sheet and describe it to everybody.

Sheet 43 can also be used as a worksheet where the pupils have to write the names of the shapes on each one or colour particular shapes a specified colour.

Name: Date:

Vocabulary Cards (3)

Sheet 44 can be photocopied onto card or laminated, then sliced on a paper cutter to produce individual flashcards. These can be used for wall displays, for example within a shapes wordbank.

Alternatively, you could supply them to the children to match with pictures of shapes. Sheet 43 could be enlarged on the photocopier then cut out to provide the separate shapes needed.

We have included some of the vocabulary which you would use with three-dimensional shapes, particularly *edge* and *face*.

shapes	square
circle	rectangle
triangle	star
pentagon	hexagon
octagon	corner
side	edge
face	straight
curved	round

The National Numeracy Strategy introduces centimetres to Year 2 pupils. Many schools will have rulers which are marked with centimetres but not millimetres:

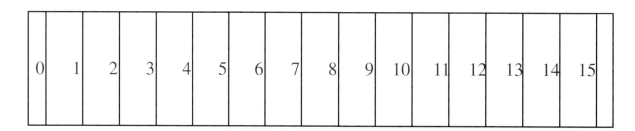

However, many children will have pencil sets of their own which contain rulers marked not only with centimetres and millimetres but also with inches. We have shown rulers like this on Sheet 45 to provide an opportunity for you to talk to the children about rulers and the way they are marked.

We suggest that Sheet 45 is photocopied onto an overhead transparency, if possible, and used as the focus for discussion during an **oral work and mental calculation** session. Show the children different rulers which you have available, explaining briefly that they are marked in different ways. Explain that they are going to work using centimetres, then discuss the rulers shown on Sheet 45. It is very important that the children see that the measurement of each line always starts from the 0 line on the ruler - some children mistakenly start from the end of the ruler or even from the 1 line.

After the discussion, the children can take a paper copy of the sheet and fill in the answers:

a about 13 cm

b about 4 cm

c about 9 cm

Check that they have these answers written correctly, then as an extension activity you could ask them to draw lines on the back of the sheet using a ruler:

about 8 cm long, about 15 cm long, about 2 cm long, about 10 cm long, etc.

Length to the Nearest Centimetre (1)

Name: Date:

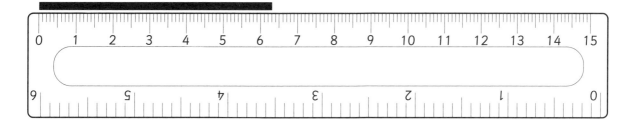

The black line is between 6 centimetres and 7 centimetres long.

The end of the line is closer to 6 centimetres so we can say that the line is about 6 centimetres long. We write it like this:

about 6 cm.

Roughly how long are these lines? Write 'about ...'

(a)

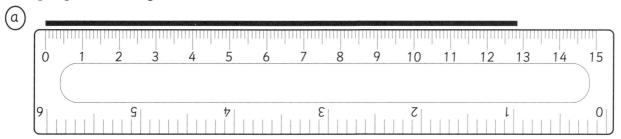

Answer:

(b)

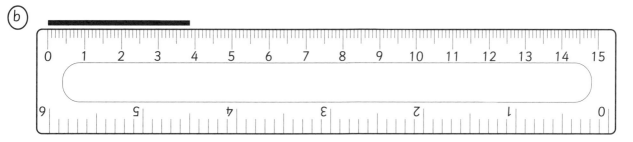

Answer:

(c)

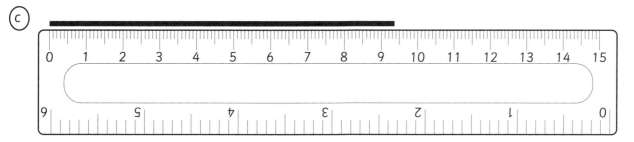

Answer:

Length to the Nearest Centimetre (2)

The National Numeracy Strategy introduces centimetres to Year 2 pupils. The children should be encouraged to make estimates of lengths. They can estimate then measure real items in the room using rulers such as this:

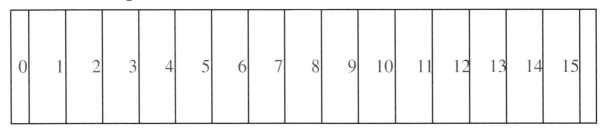

... or this:

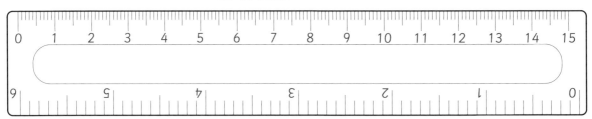

It is very important that the children see that the measurement of each line always starts from the 0 line on the ruler - some children mistakenly start from the end of the ruler or even from the 1 line.

Sheet 46 could be photocopied onto an overhead projector transparency for discussion during your **oral work and mental calculation**. After the discussion, the children can take a paper copy of the sheet to work on. The measurements of the lines, to the nearest centimetre are as follows:

      a about 15 cm

      b about 5 cm

      c about 10 cm

      d about 14 cm

      e about 8 cm

      f about 9 cm

Length to the Nearest Centimetre (2)

Name: Date:

I estimate that this line is roughly seven centimetres long …

… I measured it and found that it is about eight centimetres long.

Minnie

Max

How long are these lines, to the nearest centimetre?

Write down your estimate before you measure each line.

(a)

Estimate:	Measure:

(b)

Estimate:	Measure:

(c)

Estimate:	Measure:

(d)

Estimate:	Measure:

(e)

Estimate:	Measure:

(f)

Estimate:	Measure:

Symmetrical Reflections

The National Numeracy Strategy expects Year 2 pupils to complete symmetrical patterns where half the pattern is provided alongside a mirror line. Sheet 47 consists of a grid with several 'half-patterns' to be completed, together with a 'spare' mirror line for children to create their own symmetrical pattern.

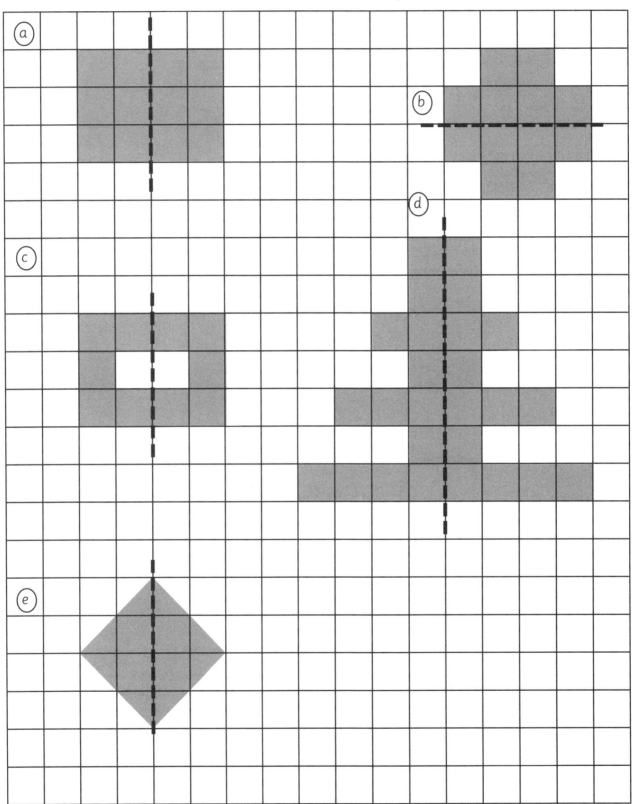

Symmetrical Reflections

Name: Date:

Draw the reflection of each of the shapes using the mirror lines shown:

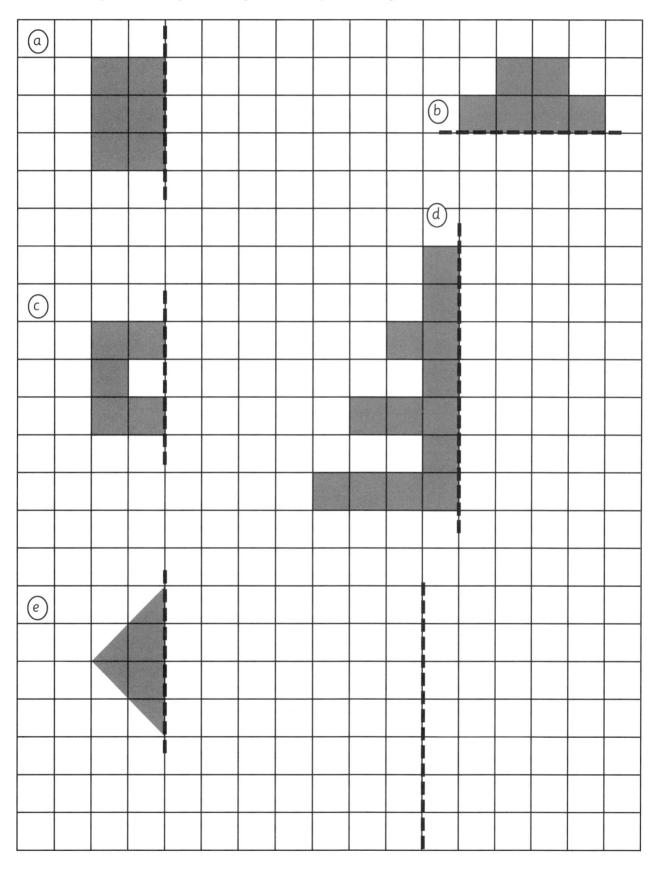

Lines of Symmetry

The National Numeracy Strategy suggests that Year 2 pupils should be able to recognise and sketch a line of symmetry in a picture.

On Sheet 48 we provide seven pictures for pupils to consider. Six of them have at least one line of symmetry. The penguin is the odd one out. The square and the rectangle both have more than one line of symmetry:

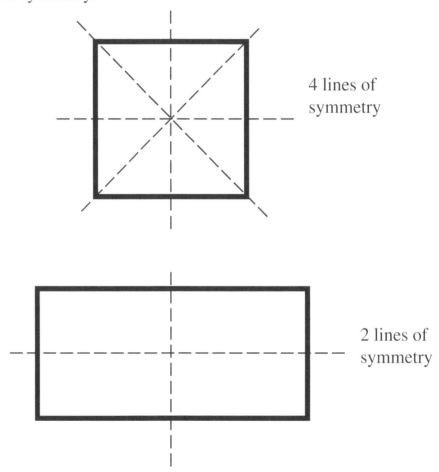

4 lines of symmetry

2 lines of symmetry

The pupils do not have to find all the lines of symmetry but should be able to sketch at least one.

You may like to photocopy Sheet 48 onto an overhead projector transparency for use in your **oral work and mental calculation** time, before copying it onto paper to give to the children as a worksheet.

Lines of Symmetry

Name: Date:

One of the pictures does not have a line of symmetry. Which one is it?

Draw a line of symmetry on all the other pictures.

Vocabulary Cards (4)

The National Numeracy Strategy supplement 'Mathematical Vocabulary' lists clearly the words which pupils are required to know and use as they progress through primary school. On Sheets 49 and 50 we have included many of the words which relate to time.

Most of the words on Sheet 49 are introduced at Reception level, though *year* and *weekend* are introduced at Year 1 and *fortnight, minute* and *second* at Year 2.

We suggest that the sheet is photocopied onto card or laminated before being cut into individual cards. These cards can be used for a wall display or for a word bank which pupils have access to. They can also be used while discussing time during **oral work and mental calculation**.

year	week
day	hour
minute	second
today	yesterday
tomorrow	weekend
fortnight	Monday
Tuesday	Wednesday
Thursday	Friday
Saturday	Sunday

Vocabulary Cards (5)

The National Numeracy Strategy supplement 'Mathematical Vocabulary' lists clearly the words which pupils are required to know and use as they progress through primary school. On Sheets 49 and 50 we have included many of the words which relate to time.

The words month, season, spring, summer, autumn and winter are introduced at Year 1, while the names of the months are introduced at Year 2.

We suggest that the sheet is photocopied onto card or laminated before being cut into individual cards. These cards can be used for a wall display or for a word bank which pupils have access to. They can also be used while discussing time during **oral work and mental calculation**.

month	season
spring	summer
autumn	winter
January	February
March	April
May	June
July	August
September	October
November	December

Clock Face and Hands

Sheet 51 provides a clock face and hands which can be photocopied onto card, then cut out to make individual clocks. The face and hands are marked with a cross where holes should be made for attaching the three pieces together with a paper fastener.

On Sheet 52 we provide another clock face but without any numerals marked on.

Clock Face and Hands

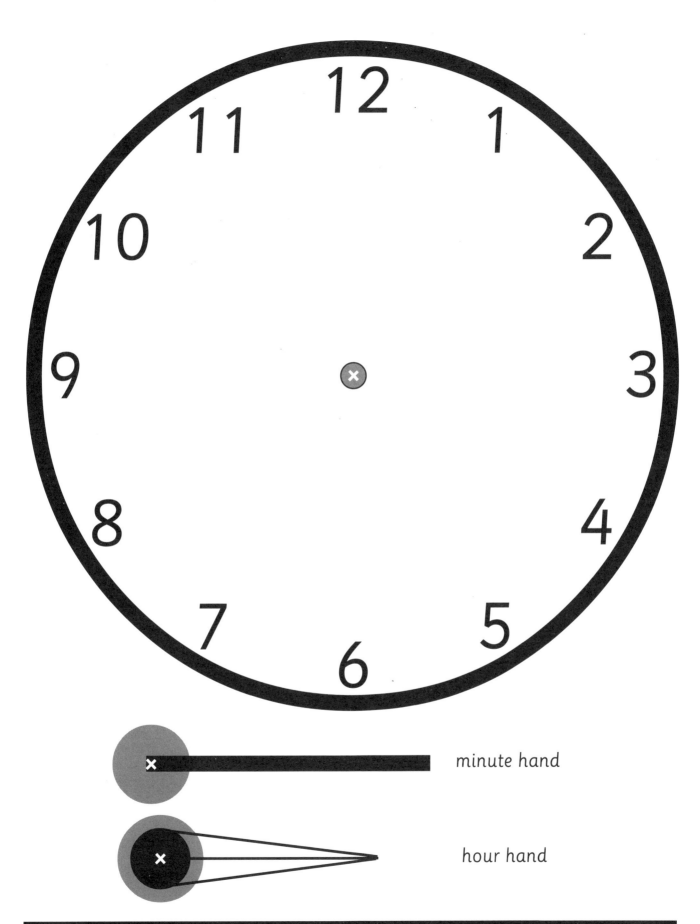

minute hand

hour hand

Blank Clock Face

Like Sheet 51, this sheet provides a clock face and hands which can be photocopied onto card, then cut out to make individual clocks. The face and hands are marked with a cross where holes should be made for attaching the three pieces together with a paper fastener.

Sheet 52 has blank spaces where the numerals should be written, though we have put in the 12 so that children can see which way up the clock goes. Writing numerals on a clock face is suggested for pupils in Reception and Year 1 within the National Numeracy Strategy.

Blank Clock Face

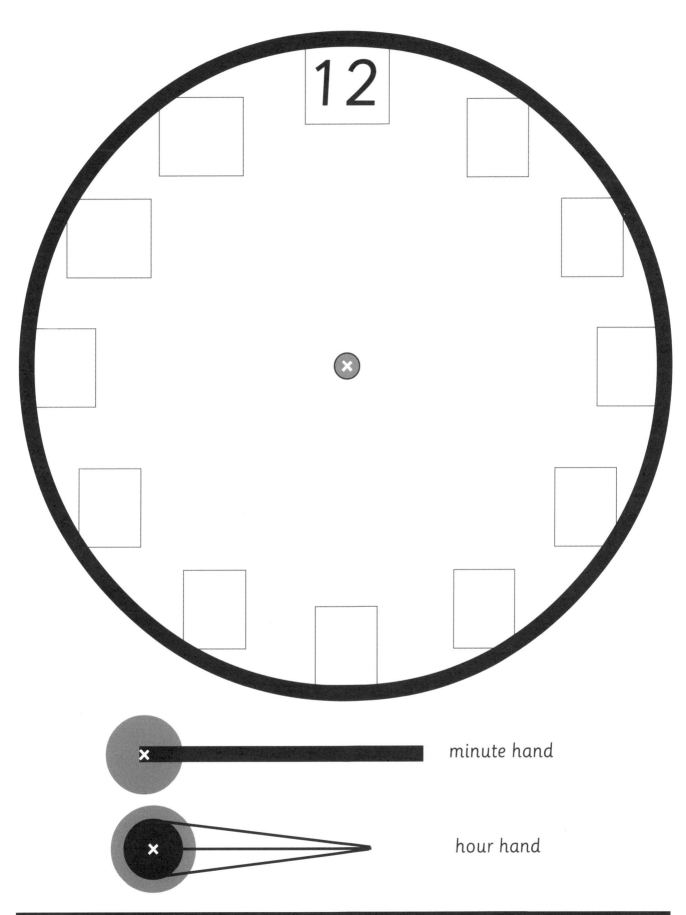

minute hand

hour hand

Clock Faces

Sheet 53 consists of a set of ten blank clock faces. We have placed each clock in a box with a question letter so that …

> … you can photocopy the sheet, then write in each box a particular time that you want children to show on the corresponding face before photocopying the number of copies required for your class or group;

> … you can photocopy the sheet, then draw hands on each clock face before photocopying the number of copies needed so that the children can write the times in the boxes;

> … you can photocopy the number you require, then ask the children to enter a time of their own choice in each box by drawing hands on the clock and writing the corresponding time in words.

Clock Faces

Name: Date:

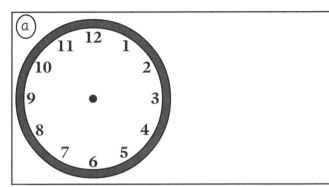 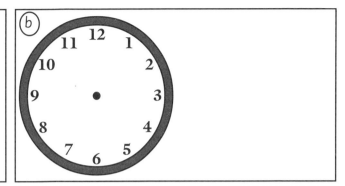

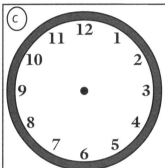 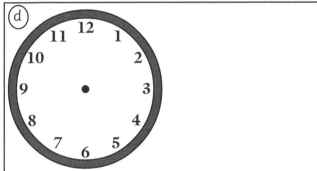

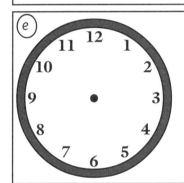 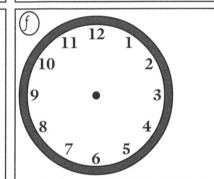

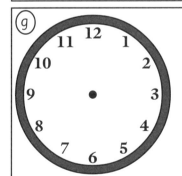 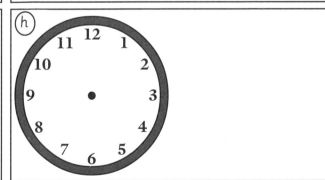

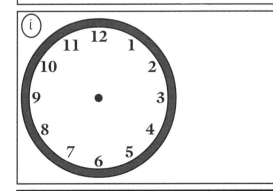 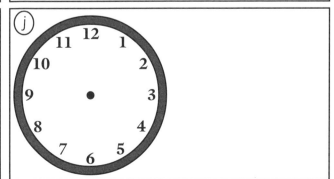

Time: O'clocks

Children can begin to learn how to read the time to the hour as early as Reception class. Sheet 54 can be photocopied onto an overhead projector transparency for use in your **oral work and mental calculation** session. It can also be copied onto paper and used as a worksheet by pupils in Year 1 or Year 2, working individually or in pairs or groups.

In oral work you could ask Year 1 or Year 2 pupils to say how many hours difference there are between pairs of clocks. For example, you could ask how many hours it is from 2 o'clock as shown on the first clock to 5 o'clock as shown on the second clock.

You may wish to enlarge one or two of the clocks on the photocopier to produce an overhead projector transparency. If you chose clock f, for example, you could ask firstly what time the clock is showing, then what time it showed an hour ago, then what it will show in an hour's time. When pupils are confident with this they may be able to answer similar questions involving half-hours. Year 2 pupils should be able to go on to discuss quarter hours.

For speed of marking, the times shown on the clocks are as follows:

b five o'clock	c nine o'clock	d six o'clock
e eleven o'clock	f four o'clock	g one o'clock
h ten o'clock	i twelve o'clock	

Time: O'clocks

Name: Date:

What time is on each clock?

two o'clock

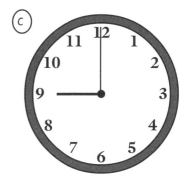

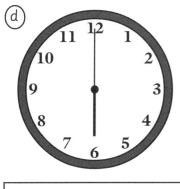

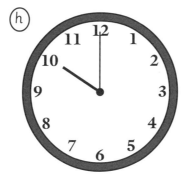

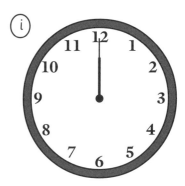

Time: Half Hours

Year 1 pupils need to be able to read the time to the hour or half hour on an analogue clock. Sheet 55 provides a set of clocks which can be photocopied onto an overhead projector transparency for use in your oral work sessions. The sheet can also be copied onto paper for pupils to work on individually or in pairs.

We have deliberately made the times on the clocks sequential. Many of the children who experience difficulty with telling the time have not grasped that we need to consider which **hour** the hour-hand last visited, to decide on what the 'past' time is. In discussing Sheet 55 with the pupils they can be encouraged to see that we are adding half an hour to each previous clock time.

For speed of marking, the times shown on the clocks are as follows:

b half past three   c four o'clock   d half past four

e five o'clock   f half past five   g six o'clock

h half past six   i seven o'clock

Time: Half Hours

Name: _____ Date: _____

What time is on each clock?

(a)

three o'clock

(b)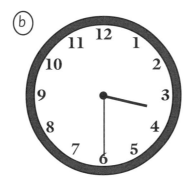

_____

(c)

_____

(d)

_____

(e)

_____

(f)

_____

(g)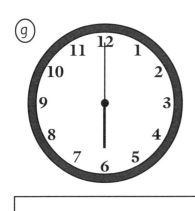

_____

(h)

_____

(i)

_____

Time: Quarter Past

Year 2 pupils need to be able to read the time to the hour, half hour or quarter hour on a digital clock or an analogue clock. Sheet 56 provides a set of clocks which can be photocopied onto an overhead projector transparency for use in your oral work sessions. The sheet can also be copied onto paper for pupils to work on individually or in pairs.

Many of the children who experience difficulty with telling the time have not grasped that we need to consider which **hour** the hour-hand last visited, to decide on what the 'past' time is. In discussing each clock on Sheet 56 you could ask the children to look carefully to see which hour the hour hand has last been to. Ideally you could show them using a real clock or a geared teaching clock where you can move the hands correctly. For example, to show a quarter past five you would show five o'clock then ask the pupils to observe exactly what happens as the hands move to quarter past: many will not have noticed before that the hour hand moves as well as the minute hand. You can make a link with fractions work by pointing out that the hour hand has moved a quarter of the way between the five digit and the six digit.

On the sheet we have asked pupils to write their answers in three different ways, to reinforce their knowledge that a quarter of an hour is made up of fifteen minutes and to begin to make the link between digital and analogue clocks. This link is made more directly on Sheet 58.

For speed of marking, the answers are as follows:

b   quarter past seven, 15 minutes past 7, 7:15
c   quarter past ten, 15 minutes past 10, 10:15
d   quarter past twelve, 15 minutes past 12, 12:15
e   quarter past six, 15 minutes past 6, 6:15
f   quarter past one, 15 minutes past 1, 1:15
g   quarter past nine, 15 minutes past 9, 9:15
h   quarter past two, 15 minutes past 2, 2:15
i   quarter past three, 15 minutes past 3, 3:15

Name: Date:

 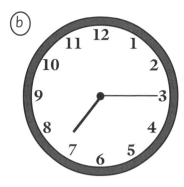 (c)

| quarter past four |
| 15 minutes past 4 |
| 4:15 |

Year 2 pupils need to be able to read the time to the hour, half hour or quarter hour on a digital clock or an analogue clock. Sheet 57 provides a set of clocks which can be photocopied onto an overhead projector transparency for use in your oral work sessions. The sheet can also be copied onto paper for pupils to work on individually or in pairs.

In discussing each clock on Sheet 57 you could ask the children firstly to look carefully to see which hour the hour hand is on its way to, then to consider which hour it last visited. Ideally you could show them using a real clock or a geared teaching clock where you can move the hands correctly. For example, to show a quarter to six you would show five o'clock then ask the pupils to observe exactly what happens as the hands move to quarter to six.

On the sheet we have asked pupils to write their answers in three different ways, to reinforce their knowledge that a quarter of an hour is made up of fifteen minutes and to begin to make the link between digital and analogue clocks. This link is made more directly on Sheet 58. Some children experience difficulty with the fact that we are saying that the time is fifteen minutes to six while one of the ways of writing the time is 5:45. This provides a good opportunity for discussing the fact that there are sixty minutes in one hour, then for considering the numerical relationships between 15, 45 and 60:

$$45 + 15 = 60$$
$$15 + 45 = 60$$
$$60 - 45 = 15$$
$$60 - 15 = 45$$

... so 45 minutes after 5 o'clock means that there are 15 minutes to 6 o'clock.

For speed of marking, the answers are as follows:

b   quarter to eleven, 15 minutes to 11, 10:45
c   quarter to one, 15 minutes to 1, 12:45
d   quarter to eight, 15 minutes to 8, 7:45
e   quarter to three, 15 minutes to 3, 2:45
f   quarter to five, 15 minutes to 5, 4:45
g   quarter to two, 15 minutes to 2, 1:45
h   quarter to twelve, 15 minutes to 12, 11:45
i   quarter to nine, 15 minutes to 9, 8:45

Time: Quarter To

Name: Date:

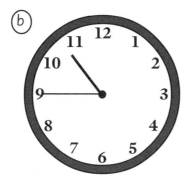

quarter to six
15 minutes to 6
5:45

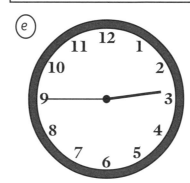

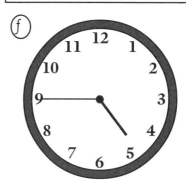

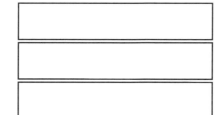

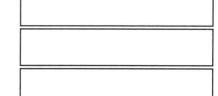

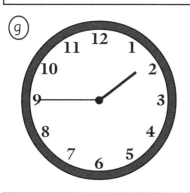

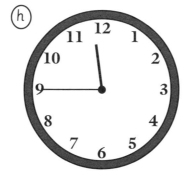

Analogue and Digital Clocks

Sheet 58 provides a set of clocks in both analogue and digital format together with times provided in writing. The Year 2 pupils' task is to enter the appropriate times by

… drawing in the hands of the analogue clocks;
… entering the time in writing;
… completing the digital times by drawing in the missing digits.

For speed of marking, these are the answers:

a quarter past six 6:15

b half past nine 9:30

c quarter past two 2:15

d quarter to seven 6:45

e quarter to two 1:45

f quarter to eleven 10:45

g quarter past twelve 12:15

h quarter to twelve 11:45

 NUMERACY TODAY
© Andrew Brodie *Publications* ✓ www.acblack.com

Analogue and Digital Clocks

Name: Date:

This is the time in writing.

half past two

This is called an analogue clock.

This is called a digital clock.

Fill in the missing information below:

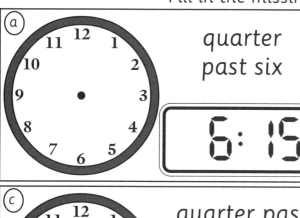

quarter past six

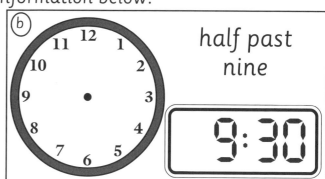

half past nine

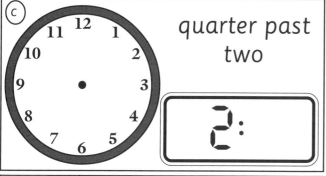

quarter past two

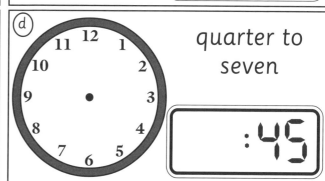

quarter to seven

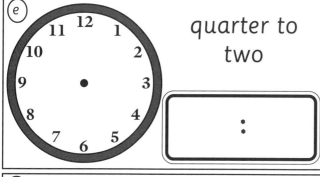

quarter to two

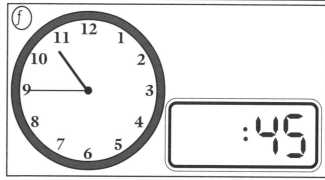

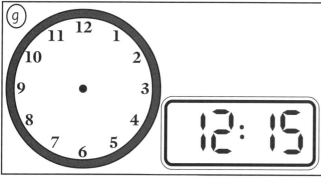

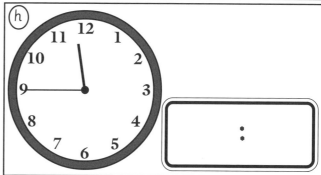

Days of the Week

Sheet 59 is designed to be used in several different ways according to the age of the pupils and the wishes of the teacher.

For Reception children:

... you could give them a photocopy of the sheet for them to practise writing the days in the right hand box;

... you could copy the sheet onto card then cut out the days of the week for the children to arrange in sequence.

For Year 1 and Year 2 children:

... you could photocopy the sheet onto an overhead projector transparency to use during your oral work session. Ask the children what day it is today and what the date is. Write the date in the middle box which is next to the appropriate day of the week and write the month in the right hand box. Now discuss tomorrow's date, then yesterday's date and the dates of the other days this week, entering the date in each middle box as appropriate. In this way the children will be practising numbers in sequence (and may need to look at a number line to help them) and they will be using appropriate vocabulary related to time.

... you could discuss, with advanced pupils, today's date, then what date it was one week ago and what date it will be in one week's time.

... you could copy the sheet onto worksheets for pupils to complete themselves.

Days of the Week

Name: _____   Date: _____

Sunday		_____
Monday		_____
Tuesday		_____
Wednesday		_____
Thursday		_____
Friday		_____
Saturday		_____

Months and Seasons

Sheet 60 is designed for Year 2 pupils, who are required to know the names and order of the months of the year.

You may wish to photocopy the sheet onto an overhead projector transparency for use during your oral work session.

You could discuss:

... the month we are in now

... last month

... next month

... the months of pupils' birthdays

... the order of the months

... the way we sometimes write the date using the number of the month

... the seasons being roughly divided into March, April and May for spring,
June, July and August for summer, etc.

Having discussed the sheet, the pupils can now complete it and perhaps add pictures in the appropriate places to represent the seasons, together with the written season words which we have included in the word bank.

Months and Seasons

Name: _____ Date: _____

Write the names of the months in the correct places.
Write the correct numbers of the months in the circles.

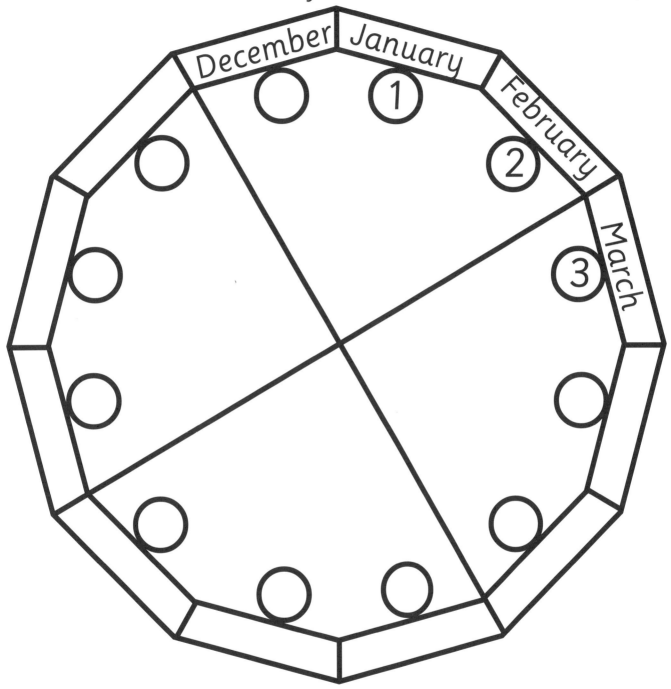

WORD BANK

April	November	August	October
July	May	September	June
autumn	spring	winter	summer

Name:

Doubles

1 + 1 = ☐
2 + 2 = ☐
3 + 3 = ☐
4 + 4 = ☐
5 + 5 = ☐
6 + 6 = ☐
7 + 7 = ☐
8 + 8 = ☐
9 + 9 = ☐

10 + 10 = ☐
11 + 11 = ☐
12 + 12 = ☐
13 + 13 = ☐
14 + 14 = ☐
15 + 15 = ☐

20 + 20 = ☐
25 + 25 = ☐
30 + 30 = ☐
35 + 35 = ☐
40 + 40 = ☐
45 + 45 = ☐

50 + 50 = ☐

Numeracy Today is published by Andrew Brodie Publications.
Andrew Brodie Publications publish a range of educational workbooks for children, available through bookstores.